GEORGES CUVIER

ZOOLOGIST

Portrait of Cuvier by Van Brae, 1798. Cuvier, recently arrived in Paris, is shown with his zoological collections and, ironically, a microscope, an instrument he but rarely employed. This splendid portrait of the young naturalist reveals none of the coldness and pompousness so characteristic of Cuvier in later years. (Muséum Archives.)

GEORGES CUVIER
ZOOLOGIST

A Study in the History of Evolution Theory

WILLIAM COLEMAN

HARVARD UNIVERSITY PRESS

Cambridge, Massachusetts

1964

Distributed in Great Britain by Oxford University Press, London

Library of Congress Catalog Card Number 64–10442

Printed in the United States of America

For my father
ROBERT GILES COLEMAN

ACKNOWLEDGMENTS

I acknowledge gladly the assistance given me by the directors and staffs of the Harvard College libraries, the Boston Public Library, the Bibliothèque Nationale, the libraries of the Muséum d'histoire naturelle, the Institut de France, the Académie des sciences, and the Wellcome Medical Historical Library. Also, the Württembergische Landesbibliothek (Stuttgart), the Universitätsbibliothek (Tübingen), the Universiteitsbibliotheek (Amsterdam), the library of the British Museum, and the libraries of The Johns Hopkins University.

The Institut de France has permitted the reproduction of lengthy texts from the *fonds Cuvier*; the illustrations were provided by the Library of the Muséum d'histoire naturelle; the Editors of the *Archives internationales d'histoire des sciences* have allowed republication of certain passages of mine which appeared previously in their journal (no. 61, 1962). I thank all individuals concerned for their courteous accord. The research upon which this book is based has been partially supported by a fellowship granted by the National Institutes of Health for the years 1960–1962. The Department of History of The Johns Hopkins University has given generous assistance in the preparation of the final manuscript.

I wish to thank the following persons for their advice, criticism and assistance: Professors H. Guerlac, J. P. Lehman, J. Piveteau, R. Taton; Drs. H. Braüning-Octavio, Théo. Cahn, M. Rooseboom, J. Théodoridès; M. Yves Laissus, Mme. P. Gauja, and Miss R. Rappaport.

I am especially indebted to Professors Georges Canguilhem, I. Bernard Cohen, Ernst Mayr, and George Gaylord Simpson. They have guided my research, criticized and improved the presentation of my conclusions, and provided necessary and constant encouragement.

Finally, my greatest thanks go to my wife and to my friends, George Basalla and Frederic L. Holmes, who have been throughout my most direct and insistent critics.

W. C.

Baltimore, Maryland
December 1963

CONTENTS

ix

CONTENTS

ILLUSTRATIONS

GEORGES CUVIER
ZOOLOGIST

NOTE ON DOCUMENTATION

The following abbreviations have been used to indicate the major collections of Cuvier manuscript material:

IFANF   Paris: Bibliothèque de l'Institut de France, *ancien et nouveau fonds*.

IFFC   Paris: Bibliothèque de l'Institut de France, *fonds Cuvier*.

MHN   Paris: Bibliothèque du Muséum d'histoire naturelle. The figures following these abbreviations refer to the catalogue numbers of each collection. See Bibliography, A.

All translations into English are mine (including the appendices).

Introduction

I n the title, *Georges Cuvier, Zoologist,* the word zoologist should
be stressed, for this is not to be a biography of the Cuvier who was
at once an educator, an administrator, and a scientist. The objective
of this book is instead to trace the major features of the French
naturalist's zoological theories and practice. Contained within this
objective is another aim, an aim which provides the central theme
of the following narrative. This theme is Cuvier's uncompromising
opposition to the hypothesis of the transmutation of biological species. By his determined advocacy of the fixity of species Cuvier was
to become one of the most significant figures in the development, or
retardation, of the new doctrines later to become known as the
theory of organic evolution.

The Jardin des Plantes in Paris, today officially the Muséum
d'histoire naturelle, enjoyed a remarkable prosperity in the years
following the French revolution. Gathered together in Paris at this
time were L. J. M. Daubenton, Buffon's aging collaborator, Etienne
Geoffroy Saint-Hilaire, a philosophical naturalist of the first order,
A. L. de Jussieu, a distinguished member of an honored family of
botanists, R. J. Haüy, a celebrated mineralogist, J. B. de Lamarck,
botanist and zoologist, and Georges Cuvier, anatomist and zoologist.
Of this famous assemblage none was more esteemed, both publicly
and professionally, than Cuvier.

Cuvier first gained fame by his treatises on animal anatomy and
classification. To him belongs the distinction of having systematically
applied structural comparison throughout the entire animal kingdom. Whereas many authors before him had compared separate
structures and, more rarely, complete bodies of animals from selected species, his pleas and, above all, his example were the moti-

vating factors which gave a new orientation to the ancient science of anatomy and made of it one of the principal modern zoological disciplines. In another realm, animal classification, Cuvier sought a complete departure from the predominant and unimaginative post-Linnaean systems and from the popular idea of a zoological *série*, or scale of being. He attempted to arrange the animal species and higher groups in an order determined by anatomical principles and general relationships. His work quickly became the standard manual of zoological systematics and remained in use, with modifications, throughout a greater part of the nineteenth century. It was for this work in animal taxonomy that Cuvier earned from his admirers the title of Legislator for the natural sciences. Paleontology was Cuvier's third area of interest and original investigation. As in comparative anatomy he was not the first to study evidence in this field. However, his researches upon the fossil remains of now extinct quadrupeds, reconstructed with the aid of anatomical and taxonomic knowledge, so thoroughly recast procedure for the study of the history of life upon the earth that the inspiration for all subsequent treatises upon vertebrate paleontology may be regarded as having originated in his successes.

Comparative anatomy, zoological classification, and the study of the fossil record formed the substance of Cuvier's scientific practice. He was also deeply concerned with the general problems facing his science. Upon the fundamental problem of the fixity or mutability of biological species Cuvier's opinion is today notorious. The sources and form of his denial of species transmutation have been, unfortunately, less commonly understood. Cuvier contributed to the modest revival in the late eighteenth century of Aristotelian biological doctrines, and the functional expression of the activities of vital phenomena which characterized his writings arose from his adoption of Aristotle's teleological conception of life. On many individual issues, for example, spontaneous generation, preformation, and the ordinal and temporal chains of being, he disagreed completely with Aristotle and, more vigorously, with his contemporary

2

opponents, Lamarck, Geoffroy, and the German *Naturphilosophen*.
His general conception of life and its phenomena, governed by
anatomicophysiological rules, is strictly Aristotelian in fact and in
intention and constituted the principal argument advanced against
the hypothesis of the transmutation of species.

Many of these issues, when considered together, have subsequently
become known as the "species problem." From at least the middle of
the eighteenth century field naturalists recognized clearly the existence and integrity of the presumably smallest practical units of biological classification, the species, and Cuvier of course also recognized this reality of the species. The "problem" was how to account
for these various species. What was their origin? Were they absolutely fixed or were they highly variable? Were the existence and
distribution of present and past species somehow related to the
events of the earth's history? Were there any past species at all,
that is, species now entirely extinct? In short, had life on the earth
had a history and, if so, what lessons might this history hold for
the general problems of zoology?

Cuvier, sometimes directly and oftentimes indirectly, suggested
answers to all of these questions. He believed that a species was to
a small degree variable but that it could never be transformed into
another and truly different species. His basically functional approach
to zoology, best expressed in the first anatomical rule ("correlation
of parts"), persuaded him that the species problem could be re-
solved. The solution which he presented was emphatically one
stated in his own terms: the functionally integrated animal, or specific *type*, could not significantly vary in any of its parts or operations
without abruptly perishing, perishing precisely because it was no
longer a fully and functionally integrated whole organism. There
existed no possible foothold for the incipient transformation of the
animal or species. The principles of comparative anatomy were
therefore considered as being as essential to the establishment of a
correct zoological philosophy (the fixity of the species) as they were
thought necessary for the accurate classification of the same species

3

and for the proper reconstruction of the debris of extinct creatures.

Cuvier was by temperament cautious and conservative and by conviction a devout Christian. He was very much aware of the already long tradition of seeking in science additional justification of the Christian doctrine and the extension into science of basically religious conceptions. Whatever interest these attempts may have held for him, he was not seduced by their superficial attractions. The religious experience he regarded as a special realm only incidentally influenced by the methods and discoveries of science. He sought only to show the absence of contradiction between scientific doctrines and religious truths. Only by gratuitous overestimation of the strength and limits of the influence of Christian doctrine on Cuvier's scientific beliefs can the historian trace his opposition to species transformation exclusively or preponderantly to the dogma of his Church.

Not the least impressive feature of Cuvier's intellectual endeavor was the over-all consistency with which he handled these diverse strands. Aristotelian zoological principles, comparative anatomy, the new science of fossils, and an ostensible adherence to the empirical manifestos of the science of the Newtonian age were brought together to form the fabric of a zoological orthodoxy which would endure until the coming of Darwin. From each attitude and from the factual stores of his science he was able to extract the materials necessary for an apparently final solution to the species problem. A study of Cuvier's scientific thought must therefore undertake to treat in detail each element of his work and yet remember constantly that these same elements had their individual roles in the total complex of his ideas.

I

~~~~~~~~

Backgrounds

*Will you never learn that it is necessary
to explain a man's words by his character,
and not his character by his words?*

— J. J. ROUSSEAU [1]

A CONVICTION that the phenomena of the natural world were ultimately reducible to simple and exact description and explanation
was an essential feature of Cuvier's intellectual outlook. He felt that
the physical universe was both orderly and lawful and he believed
it to be the primary task of the natural philosopher to attempt to
discover the laws which lay behind the confusing appearances wit-
nessed by the casual observer. He believed his own task to be the
discovery of the particular laws of nature which were applicable to
the existence and behavior of the animals.

Cuvier was in many ways a child of the Enlightenment. He ap-
plauded the capacities of the human mind with the same fervor
with which he stressed the advantages of the virtuous life. He was
not an adventurous thinker. He sought principally to cut through
prior obscurities and misinterpretation and to erect thereby a new
science of zoology on simple, clear, and precise principles. He found
the works of Linnaeus and Buffon to be most congenial but still
inadequate models for the reform of his science and he supplemented their instruction by extensive reading of the Aristotelian
biological works. His education, directed toward preparation for a
career in the natural sciences, was both classical and modern and

it gave him at an early age advantages which contemporary naturalists could not hope to equal. The ideals and attitudes gained from early experiences remained with Cuvier throughout his life and his scientific thought is singularly free from development and evolution. His talents and training, together with great and undisguised ambitions, served him well as he quickly ascended the ladder of scientific success and social and official favor.

Georges Cuvier (1769–1832)

Born (23 August 1769) in the small French-speaking, predominantly Lutheran town of Montbéliard (Doubs), then attached to the Duchy of Württemberg, Cuvier did not until 1793 officially become a French citizen. His family had been located in eastern France since the mid-sixteenth century and had settled in Montbéliard in the early 1700's. They had been faithful members of the Lutheran Church almost since the age of the Reformation itself and it was traditional that one son in the family always be trained for the Protestant ministry. Cuvier's grandfather was a court clerk (*greffier*) and his father, after a long and distinguished military career, had retired to Montbéliard to serve as commandant of the local artillery. A late marriage brought him three sons, Georges-Charles-Henry (1765–1769), Jean-Léopold-Nicolas-Frédéric (1769–1832), and Georges-Frédéric (1773–1838). After the early death of the eldest son and probably before the birth of Georges-Frédéric (known as "Frédéric" Cuvier) the name "Georges" was adopted by Jean, and it is by the legally inaccurate name Georges Cuvier that he has since been known. His first teacher was his mother. She guided her precocious son in his studies and compelled him to develop and to refine his considerable talents as a draftsman. He early cultivated an interest in natural history and, in addition, formed the usual child's collections of natural curiosities. In the primary schools of Montbéliard he was an exemplary student, mastering civil and religious history, Latin and Greek, geography and mathematics, all with equal ease.[2]

The family plans that Georges become a minister were frustrated by an unsympathetic teacher, but the boy's reputation brought him to the attention of Karl Eugen, then Duke of Württemberg. The Duke had founded at Stuttgart a school for the training of the most talented young men of his territories. Military in character, with uniforms, barracks, and rigid discipline, the Académie Caroline (Karlsschule) offered a program of general studies and advanced instruction in various special fields, for example, military science, forest management, commerce, and law, all placed in a predominantly Christian context. Moral instruction was a prime concern from the beginning of the students' studies. "One begins," said Batz in the very year of Cuvier's entrance into the Académie, "by teaching them the pure doctrine of the Evangile and by explaining to them the moral truths drawn from the nature of man and his relationships [and] by showing them their duties towards God, towards their neighbor, and towards themselves." Cuvier selected administration as the area of his studies, primarily because it was under this faculty that natural history was included. During his years at the Académie (1784–1788) he studied law, chemistry, mineralogy, zoology and botany, the science of mines, police, *chancellerie*, commerce, finance, practical and theoretical economics, and geometry. Formal instruction in natural history was in abeyance during Cuvier's period of residence. He nevertheless profited from the activity of a small student natural history society and also from personal instruction from K. F. Kielmeyer, later a regular instructor at the Académie and the author of a seminal essay in the naissant German *Naturphilosophie* (*Über die Verhältnisse der organischen Kräfte* [Stuttgart, 1793]). Cuvier later recalled that it was Kielmeyer who had taught him how to dissect and had given him his first ideas in "philosophical natural history." [3]

Liberal in tone, stimulating and well-regulated in practice, placing the improvement of the student before all other considerations, the Académie Caroline was a singularly fortunate institution for the young Cuvier. He continued always to admire its careful blend of classical study in the ancient languages and philosophy with the modern disciplines of living languages, administration, and science. The completion of study at the Académie ended his formal instruction and began, unexpectedly, seven years (1788–1795) of equally successful self-education. The training at Stuttgart had prepared him for service in the Duke's administration. At graduation, however, no positions were available and the young man discovered himself to be without occupation. There was no opportunity to remain at home in expectation of a call to the Duke's services since the financial crisis then facing France, an external sign of the political bankruptcy which marked the end of the *ancien régime*, had first reduced and then eliminated his father's small pension. The family, almost without income, could scarcely afford the luxury of a well-educated but unemployed son. Happily, he soon had the good fortune to replace another *montbéliardois* as tutor to the son of the d'Héricys, a Protestant noble family living in Normandy.

In Caen and in the Norman countryside Cuvier passed the violent years of the French Revolution, an observer at first sympathetic to the movement, but, as outrage and lawlessness increased, becoming more critical of its possible achievements and totally disgusted by its methods. Cuvier was never a politician, being temperamentally too remote from the personal and frequently unpleasant demands of politics, and he was perhaps not convinced that political action was not really a vain aspect of human activity. When he entered public affairs he did so as an administrator, seeking only to organize and to regulate the public effort. He first tasted public administration when appointed secretary-clerk to the tiny Norman commune of Bec-aux-Cauchois, a position which he occupied from 10 November 1793 until 19 February 1795. Not only was he responsible for maintaining contact with the Parisian authorities and keeping the village records, but he was also obliged to deliver pious Republican patriotic addresses, to help collect saltpeter, and to "maintain liberty and equality or to die at his post." [4]

The years in Normandy were years of intensive work in natural history. It was here that Cuvier became a full-time naturalist. He thoroughly investigated the flora and fauna of the Norman landscape, but it was ultimately the seashore which came to dominate his time and thought. This was his first acquaintance with the sea and he had no desire to waste this unique opportunity. He wrote to his Stuttgart friend, Pfaff, that at Fiquainville, the d'Héricy's country estate, he would be "nothing but a naturalist." [5] Cuvier delighted in the wealth and diversity of the marine fauna and, taking the popular conception of Aristotle as his example, he turned to preparing repeated and intricate dissections and recording by accurate drawings all that he observed. The class of Mollusks especially attracted his interest; investigations made in Normandy laid the foundations for his superb series of monographs on members of this group, masterpieces of descriptive anatomy which he published only after settling in Paris. Birds, plants, and innumerable invertebrate animals were also examined and the letters sent to Pfaff are swelled with discussions of such topics as the suction feet of the starfishes and lengthy lists of insects observed at Fiquainville.

These years of apprenticeship came to a close in the spring of 1795. The *abbé* Tessier, a renowned agricultural expert taking refuge in the provinces during the Terror, upon meeting Cuvier at an agricultural assembly in Valmont immediately recognized the young naturalist's great ability and wrote of him to his associates remaining in Paris. To his friend A. L. de Jussieu he addressed the following commendation (10 February 1795):

At the sight of this young man I experienced the astonishment of the philosopher who, cast upon an unknown shore, saw traced there geometrical figures. You recall that it was I who gave Delambre to the Academy; in another area, this young man will be another Delambre.[6]

The result of this correspondence was an invitation to Cuvier to join and share the vigorous scientific activity of the French capital. Receiving assurances that in Paris his future would be secure and yielding to the flattering demands of the Parisian savants, Cuvier left Normandy and arrived in Paris, henceforth his home, in March 1795.

From 1795 until his death (13 May 1832) Cuvier's abundant energies were consumed by three interrelated careers, education, administration, and science. Although the last is of principal importance for the consideration of the naturalist's scientific attitudes, his work in education and administration reveals interesting facets of his personality and intellectual outlook. Cuvier saw in public instruction an opportunity both to improve the intellectual qualities of the French nation and to impress upon the yet ignorant masses the ideals of respect for the law, acquiescence to the demands of the constituted authorities, and regular and attentive fulfillment of social responsibilities. He favored secular instruction, including much natural science, and fiercely opposed all efforts by the Roman Catholic brotherhoods to introduce their instructors into the public classrooms. His opposition to the Jesuits in particular became almost an obsession. For over a decade he acted as an imperial Inspector of public instruction and he served on the council of the Napoleonic Université de France from its inception (1808) until his death. Moreover, in 1803 he was named, with Delambre, one of the two *secrétaires perpétuels* of the Académie des sciences of the new Institut de France. Bonaparte appointed him to the Conseil d'état in 1813 and he remained there (with the exception of the Hundred Days in 1815) until 1832. In 1817 he assumed a vice presidency of the Ministry of Interior and, eleven years later, was made director of all non-Catholic churches in France. The great passion of his life, it was rumored, was not zoology but the daily minutiae of administrative affairs.[7]

All of these activities naturally enough provided ample occasion for Cuvier to exercise his ambition of introducing order and clarity into the confused human world. He was less concerned with the desires and actions of political persons than with the institutions within which these figures acted. For example, during the *Restauration*, a golden age in France for freedom of expression and apparent parliamentary power, Cuvier worked vigorously with Guizot on the preparation and enactment of new laws of censorship. This, he protested, was done to protect France from the extremists of the Right and the Left, but it is significant that his conception of protection found its immediate form in the extension of the power of central authority.[8] Cuvier was a political conservative. His greatest fear and, considering the chaos of life during and following much of the era of the Revolution and First Empire, a very understandable fear, was social disorder. Political upheaval meant to him the decline of opportunities for the happy life and for creative intellectual activity. His efforts in public administration and in education were thus devoted to securing a strong social order and to training the youth of the nation to cherish and to preserve this order.

Cuvier, perhaps better than any other naturalist of the early nineteenth century, was able to maintain a firm and comprehensive grasp of all relevant facts and yet never lose sight of zoology's need for generalization. This ability is fully apparent in the truly enormous literary production so characteristic of his scientific career: in forty years he published more than 300 scientific articles and was principal author of at least five major multivolume monographs. His earliest published writings, two memoirs on the insects, antedate his arrival in Paris while his final efforts (on the history of science), if not his exact words, continued to appear long after his death.

The most brilliant years of his scientific career, the period of innovation, voluminous publication, and early success, embrace the first two decades in Paris, roughly 1795–1812. In collaboration with his friend and colleague, Etienne Geoffroy Saint-Hilaire, he published in 1795 a basic memoir on mammalian classification and, separately, two essays on the classification of the so-called "insects," which include his earliest statements on general systematics and tentative attempts to distribute meaningfully the organisms in question (see Bibliography, B, for all full-title references). Three years later, while lecturing at the Ecole centrale, he became aware of the need for a comprehensive and popular textbook of zoology. In answer to this demand, the *Tableau élémentaire d'histoire naturelle des animaux* (1798), a large, illustrated treatise and Cuvier's first book, was written and it received an immediate welcome. In the last years of the century Cuvier was appointed *suppléant* to Mertrud at the Muséum d'histoire naturelle; he became titular professor of comparative anatomy in 1802. During this period he had begun his famous series of lectures on comparative anatomy but did not have enough time to prepare them for publication. The task of collecting and editing the notes was undertaken by others and the first two volumes of the *Leçons d'anatomie comparée* appeared in 1800, the concluding three volumes being issued in 1805. In addition to these works on zoology and anatomy, Cuvier had been engaged since 1796 in the study of fossil bones and had produced numerous memoirs treating often previously unknown specimens. These memoirs were collected and published in 1812 as the *Recherches sur les ossemens fossiles des quadrupèdes*. Appended to the first volume of this elegant folio edition was Cuvier's most popular writing, the *Discours préliminaire*, commonly but wrongly called the "theory of the earth." The *Discours* was later (1821) rewritten for a new edition of the *Recherches* and was then issued separately (1825); it now bore the title *Discours sur les révolutions de la surface du globe*. This essay was the product of several lecture series delivered at the Collège de France where, since 1800, Cuvier had held Daubenton's old chair of general natural history.

Cuvier excused himself from strictly scientific work in 1807 and 1808 in order to prepare, for the Institut and at the command of Bonaparte, a report on the progress of the natural sciences since 1789, a work now become invaluable for the study of the history of that period. Again for the Institut, he prepared annual reports on the progress of the sciences during the preceding year.[9] Political distractions reduced the flow of scientific work after 1812 and the long-proposed issue of a compendium of systematic and descriptive zoology was delayed until 1817. The *Règne animal, distribué d'après son organisation* (1817), presenting in greatly expanded and revised form the over-all plan of the *Tableau élémentaire*, appeared in five thick, octavo volumes which attempted to include almost every animal then known. Quickly translated into many languages, it became the standard zoological manual for most of Europe and passed through numerous editions.

Cuvier realized that, although comprehensive texts may be useful and necessary, the science of zoology also demanded the preparation of detailed monographs on various special groups of animals. In Normandy and at Marseilles, and then at the Muséum, he had directed his attention to the fishes; they seem to have been his favorite animals. Now, after the *Règne animal* had been completed, he was free to turn all his energies toward an exhaustive study of this single class of animals. Before his death, with the assistance of Achille Valenciennes he had produced the first eight volumes of the great series on the fishes, the *Histoire naturelle des poissons*.

The concern of so many of these works with classification is noteworthy for, in zoology too, can be seen Cuvier's devotion to putting things in order and to leaving behind neither gaps nor uncertainties in our knowledge. This *esprit de méthode* was obvious even in his manner of research and writing. Charles Lyell, the English geologist, has accurately and fully recorded the smooth mechanism of Cuvierian research, and at the same time provided an amusing first-hand account of the methodical and orderly character of the man. In a letter from Paris to his sister, Lyell wrote:

I got into Cuvier's sanctum sanctorum yesterday, and it is truly characteristic of the man. In every part it displays that extraordinary power of methodising which is the grand secret of the prodigious feats which he performs annually without appearing to give himself the least trouble. But before I introduce you to this study, I should tell you that there is first the museum of natural history opposite his house, and admirably arranged by himself, then the anatomy museum connected with his dwelling. In the latter is a library disposed in a suite of rooms, each containing works on one subject. There is one where there are all the works on ornithology, in another room all on icthyology, in another osteology, in another *law* books, etc. etc. When he is engaged in such works as require continual reference to a variety of authors, he has a stove shifted into one of these rooms, in which everything on that subject is systematically arranged, so that in the same work he often makes the round of many apartments. But the ordinary studio contains no bookshelves. It is a longish room, comfortably furnished, lighted from above, and furnished with eleven desks to stand to, and two low tables, like a public office for so many clerks. But all is for one man, who multiplies himself as author, and admitting no one into this room, moves as he finds necessary, or as fancy inclines him, from one occupation to another. Each desk is furnished with a complete establishment of inkstand, pens, etc., pins to pin MSS. together, the works immediately in reading and the MS. in hand, and on shelves behind all the MSS. of the same work. There is a separate bell to several desks. The low tables are to sit at when he is tired. The collaborators are not numerous, but always chosen well. They save him every mechanical labour, find references, etc., are rarely admitted to the study, receive orders, and speak not.[10]

Whether he was observing and writing in the anatomy laboratory, presiding at the Institut, or pursuing any of his multifarious other activities, Cuvier's mind repelled any suggestion of vagueness or discord. All natural phenomena, like those of society and instruction, must be subjected to the rule of law; the political empire had its counterpart in the intellectual empire. Cuvier, with his contemporaries, found congenial standards in Imperial Rome — order, universality, strength, authority of the law — and, again with his generation, he tried to introduce into a chaotic and confused France some portion, however superficial, of these ancient ideals. His mental habits furthermore permitted him to realize his plan for the systematization of scientific facts. His able draftsmanship was coupled with a truly prodigious memory. He was efficient, disciplined, and austere. He was, in short, convinced that a peaceful and orderly mind was a correct mind, just as the peaceful and orderly society was the correct society.

The species problem, especially in the early nineteenth century, became intimately linked to efforts to draw support from the sciences for Christian dogma. Later (Chapter VII) it will be argued that

religious objectives played at best a very minor role in the motivation of Cuvier's opposition to the transformation hypothesis. Nevertheless, it is essential for an appreciation of Cuvier's character to
grasp at the outset certain fundamental features of his religious
attitudes. This is not an easy task, nor can it be pursued with certainty, for the naturalist's viewpoint must be inferred from the circumstances of his religious upbringing and from infrequent and
usually indirect references in his published works. His failure to
discuss publicly these questions was wholly consistent with his
general religious viewpoint.[11]

It is clear that Cuvier regarded an individual's religious convictions as being that person's private and inalienable property and
therefore in no way a fit subject for public review or criticism.
What was true with regard to all questions of first principles was
equally true of religious issues: mere discussion became a perilous
affair because man's inherent and insuperable ignorance of these
matters only permitted erroneous opinion to prevail. Such had been
the consequences, Cuvier believed, of the injudicious behavior of
Joseph Priestley, the chemist and nonconformist preacher chased
from Birmingham.

Cuvier reflected earnestly upon this alarming example and concluded that Priestley, a "rash theologian" who had "approached
with boldness the most mysterious questions," despised the "belief
of the ages," and "rejected the most revered authority," had illustrated only too clearly the danger to man of unlimited speculation.
There must exist, Cuvier knew, definite limits to religious and
philosophical enquiry. "Besides," he demanded, "is there not some
utility in seeing, by facts, to what degree the best minds may suffer
themselves to be diverted, when they forsake those limits which
Providence has marked out for the human understanding?" Cuvier's *éloge* argued that Priestley, by attacking the orthodox and
blasting the incredulous, had gone too far. Some questions were
best not subjected to rational analysis. They were beyond its capa-
bilities and, in order to assure peace, men must adhere to accepted

and traditional beliefs and practices. Cuvier was convinced that "unregulated piety" was the real source of Priestley's woe and that his greatest error had been to give too much weight to "particular opinions" on controversial subjects, forgetting that the most important of all sentiments was the "love of peace." [12]

Cuvier's personal religion was notably free from metaphysical speculation and was chiefly concerned with individual belief and the reign of virtue. Natural religion had no appeal for him. Faith, he believed, was a far more dependable support for religion than was reason. Religion, furthermore, was based on faith and not on "constraint," [13] by which Cuvier meant the action of the formal ecclesiastical and theological authorities of the Roman Catholic church. His was a practical Christianity which looked to correct behavior as the fundamental concern of the believer. Moral law alone would act to constrain the violence of men and lead them successfully towards virtue. Virtue, it appears, meant disinterested actions, the implementation of the Golden Rule.

Who can . . . uncover so many excellent deeds and not cry out that those distressing theories [in which ambition is praised] are only horrible paradoxes, and that the love of our fellow man, the pleasure in his pleasures, the suffering in his suffering, which religion places at the first rank of Christian virtues, is also the primary inclination with which nature provides us? [14]

There is little novelty in these ideas. Hume and Kant had emphasized the role of the sentiment in the religious experience and the latter, to whose critical philosophy Cuvier was greatly indebted, had also stressed the moral sanctions implicit in one's actions toward his neighbors. By birth, education, and conviction a devout Lutheran, Cuvier was not inspired to use his reason to reach his God but first to believe in God and only then to investigate the meaning of His word and His works for the human situation.

Despite the oversimplification that it brings to complex circumstances, the so-called Protestant ethic is suggestive of the formation of Cuvier's general religious and philosophical attitudes. This ethic has been characterized as "the positive estimation by Protestants of a hardly disguised utilitarianism, of intramundane interests, of a thoroughgoing empiricism, of the right and even duty of *libre-examen*, and of the explicit individual questioning of authority . . . congenial to the same values found in modern science." [15] Certainly worldly, utilitarian interests and a rabid devotion to "empiricism" were hallmarks of Cuvier's character. Other values than these also seemed to come to him from his social and religious background. The conscientious fulfillment of one's calling in life, whatever it may be, and the high esteem for the law in Lutheranism appear to have influenced him. Even the right and duty of free examination, if confined to appropriate issues, received his approval. But it was evident that Priestley had overextended himself and others would do just the same if the legitimate subjects of inquiry were not clearly defined. If in the sciences authority could be fairly questioned, in religion and political affairs authority must be regarded as the source of wisdom and social stability and therefore necessarily beyond the unrestrained probing of the curious. No man, Cuvier believed, could rightfully arrogate to himself the privilege of criticizing the established religious and social powers.

The common themes — orderliness, rationality, tranquility — which permeated Cuvier's social, political, and religious ideas reappeared without modification in his scientific work. It is curious to reflect that his greatest fame came as the result of a theory of presumably horrendous geological cataclysms, while in reality he found his intellectual ideals in the harmonious change and resultant stability of the physical and animate universe which was one of the products of popular post-Newtonian science. First instructed by the writings of Linnaeus and Buffon and taking his inspiration from their example, Cuvier was not reluctant to suggest that one day natural history, too, would have its Newton.[16] He could recommend no one more strongly for this honor than himself.

Linnaeus, Buffon, and natural history

Natural history in the eighteenth century greatly needed its Newton. The classificatory successes of John Ray and a few others in the final decades of the previous century were recognized as the starting point for any new taxonomic system, but they could be no more than a starting point. Part of the problem lay in the sheer bulk of the new plant and animal specimens then reaching Europe. Facing phenomena of enormous extent and even greater diversity, zoology and botany were painfully embarrassed by the very richness of their evidence. Swelled by collections gathered since the Renaissance — the work of exploratory expeditions, individual travelers, colonial agents, and others — the innumerable natural history cabinets of Europe increased their holdings at an extraordinary rate. The number of botanical species catalogued, one index of the trend, grew stupendously. In 1542, De L'Obel described 500 species; only eighteen years later, Bauhin listed some 5200 different kinds of plants.[17] Although the literal precision of these and the following figures is perhaps questionable, they are useful in indicating the trend in the accumulation of botanical species. Tournefort (1688) catalogued some 10,000 different kinds of plants and soon afterward John Ray raised this figure to 18,000. Linnaeus, in 1757, listed only 6200 species. The great reduction in numbers was due to his efforts to halt the practice of erecting a new species upon almost every individual new specimen received and to make of the species a more homogeneous and coherent unit. Still the new plants flooded into Europe. The number of Linnaean genera almost doubled between 1757 and 1797 and the number of species rose to 20,000 in 1805 and to 50,000 in 1824 (De Candolle). Although not with the same prodigality, new species of animals also were discovered and shipped to the collectors of Europe. To catalogue this deluge of new animals and plants usefully and accurately became one of the major tasks of natural history, and their abundance and diversity required something more than mere hasty enumeration.

In keeping with the ideal of Newtonianism it was apparent to the naturalists of the Enlightenment that a new or improved classificatory system would not alone provide satisfaction. Newtonianism was predicated on the existence of clear and precise laws governing the events of the physical universe.[18] If natural history were ever to attain the clarity and rigor which marked the triumph of Newtonian physical science, it was obvious that this advance would be due to the discovery of the order and essential lawfulness of the organic world. The advance was begun by a thorough and provocative reconsideration of the general principles of classificatory procedure and was continued by attempts to apply the new or revised methods to the distribution of all creatures without exception. This was the work by which Carolus Linnaeus and G. L. Leclerc, comte de Buffon, in Cuvier's opinion the two greatest naturalists of the century, recast the bases of animal natural history.

Linnaeus (1707–1778) was essentially a taxonomist whose primary objective was the complete systematization of organic nature. Believing that botany and zoology must make a decision between system and chaos he declared: "A system is a clue to guide us to botany, without which any such guide is a *chaos*, or a rude and indigested heap of confusion." [19] The botanist's problem thus became one of creating a system, that is, a comprehensive, convenient, and clear classification of the organisms.

To the question, What is the best system? Linnaeus gave two answers. Although perhaps not contradictory, they were at best ambiguous and ill-defined. These two systems were the natural and the artificial classifications. In the former, the naturalist attempted to preserve to the greatest possible degree the "affinities" between the various organisms which he studied. He strove to make his system a reflection of organic relationships, remote or close, and based upon the structure, behavior, and habitat of creatures in nature. A natural system also had to be a convenient guide for description and identification. A radical artificial system rejected any intention of representing the affinities of its subjects. Here the taxonomist selected conspicuous, reasonably unvarying characteristics of the organisms as his guide and disavowed all interest in the over-all habit of the specimen and its relations with its neighbors. Convenience and accuracy in identification were the advantages of this practical system. Linnaeus was aware of this distinction, as valid today as it was in the eighteenth century, and of its significance for plant science. In the *Elements of botany*, after reviewing the botanical systems of Ray, Haller, Tournefort, and Cesalpino, he declared:

> Besides all the above mentioned systems and methods of distributing plants deduced from the fructification, and which may therefore be called artificial, there is a natural method, or nature's system, which we ought diligently to endeavour to find out . . . And that this system is no *chimera*, as some may imagine, will appear, as from other considerations, so in particular from hence, that all plants, of what order soever, shew an affinity to some others to which they are nearly allied. In the mean time, till the whole of nature's method is compleatly discovered (which is much to be wished), we must be content to make use of the best artificial systems now in use.[20]

Linnaeus prepared lists of genera and orders which he considered natural, but he did not more fully develop this approach. Nature might indeed be an orderly and coherent whole, but Linnaeus knew that man still lived in ignorance and that he had to be content to impose his own creation upon nature. The natural system remained the naturalist's true goal, but until it was attained the artificial system must prevail.

Linnaeus' artificial classifications were arbitrary but not at all capricious. Their rationale was found in the idea, ascribed by Linnaeus to William Harvey, that all life must necessarily arise only from preexisting life. This notion, accepted in a "literal, realistic sense," demonstrated that there existed an uninterrupted and unaltered sequence of reproductively and morphologically distinct organisms extending from the creation to the present time. God had given each creature its own seed and had directed each to reproduce only its own kind. Spontaneous generation was patently impossible.

Cuvier, successful and content, in the attire of the Académie des sciences, 1820's. Cuvier assisted in the design of this elaborate and colorful (green and gold) ceremonial costume. (Muséum Archives.)

View of the Muséum d'histoire naturelle in 1827. Display and work galleries are to the left, public and experimental gardens at the right, and in the distance rises an artificial hillock upon which rest the Belvédère and Daubenton's grave. (Muséum Archives, courtesy of J. Théodoridès.)

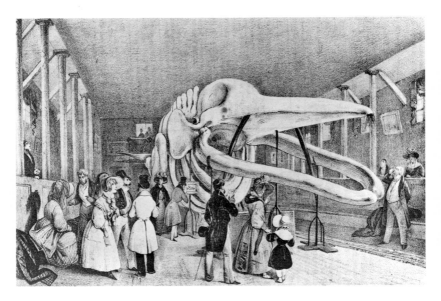

The great whale in the ancienne Galérie d'anatomie comparée, 1830. The reorganization of this gallery and the preparation of mounted specimens for display within it were perhaps Cuvier's greatest contributions to the Muséum. Note the carpets provided for fashionable visitors. (Muséum Archives.)

Portrait of J. B. de Lamarck (1744–1829), Cuvier's principal intellectual opponent. Lamarck was a masterly systematic botanist and zoologist and enjoyed perhaps the most creative mind of any of the Parisian naturalists. Cuvier, unfortunately, praised Lamarck the taxonomist while ridiculing mercilessly his speculations upon the species question. (Muséum Archives.)

Portrait of Etienne Geoffroy Saint-Hilaire (1772–1844), anatomist and philosophical naturalist. The impetuous Geoffroy and the conservative Cuvier differed profoundly on first principles, and the early cordial association between the two men rapidly dissolved into prolonged quarrels over scientific matters. (Muséum Archives.)

The Muséum also possessed a menagerie where the savants and the public could observe living creatures. The introduction of the first giraffe into the collections (shown here; 1830's) was the cause of great wonderment and pleasure. (Muséum Archives, courtesy of J. Théodoridès.)

These ideas led to Linnaeus's emphasis upon the taxonomic importance of the reproductive parts. From Cesalpino, who had based his botanical inquiries upon Aristotelian teachings, Linnaeus learned that the "final cause" of plants was propagation and that reproduction was thus the essential function of the plant. The Swedish naturalist stressed vigorously the relative importance of the organs of fructification. These parts were, in addition, especially useful because they were conspicuous, intricate, and more or less constant, and hence formed admirable concentrations of excellent taxonomic characters. Analyzing the reproductive structures, Linnaeus assigned primacy to the "number, proportion, figure, and situation" of the anthers (male), which determined the classes, and the pistils (female), which determined the orders. The sequence of plant "essences" was indicated by the following *précis*:

> The essence of vegetables [consists] in the fructification . . .
> The essence of fructification [consists] in the flower and fruit.
> The essence of the fruit consists in the seed.
> The essence of the seed consists in the *antherae* and *stigma*.[21]

From function, propagation, Linnaeus advanced to structure, the sexual parts, and on the basis of the latter he constructed his enormous tabulations of the botanical world, for example, *Genera plantarum* (1742), *Classes plantarum* (1747), and *Species plantarum* (1753). The Linnaean taxonomy is an artificial classification in which there is a peculiar blend of the elements of the sexual system and the observed features of the flowering plants.

In sharp contrast to Linnaeus, Buffon (1707–1788) denied not only the utility of animal classification but the impossibility of such creations. He was convinced that the so-called higher taxonomic categories such as the family or order, and even the genus, had no reality in nature and were only artificial constructions of the taxonomist. Buffon acknowledged the reality in nature of individuals only. He proclaimed that "in general the more we wish to augment the number of divisions of natural productions, the more we approach truth, since there really exist in nature only individuals, and the genera, orders, and classes exist only in our imaginations." The higher categories were thus rejected as being abusive to nature. The species was a more fugitive category. Buffon did not understand it to be so much a taxonomic group, in the old, static sense of this word, as it was a dynamic and temporal unit. He seems to have believed that the individual and the species comprised complementary concepts. Imagine the temporal succession of many similar individuals, then think of an unprecedentedly long persistence of one individual — was there a difference? No, answered Buffon, and the species was really no more than our image of this extended "individual." [22]

Buffon was not thoroughly consistent in this argument, for, on other occasions, he attempted to provide a definition of the species in terms of the reproductive incompatibilities between different kinds of animals. The reproductive gap seemed to indicate that there did exist discrete groups of animals which, in regard to fertility at least, behaved as if they belonged to different and clearly distinguishable species. Furthermore, in the descriptions given in the *Histoire naturelle générale et particulière*, Buffon used nothing but the familiar and commonly accepted zoological taxonomic categories. Without hesitation he spoke of the quadrupeds, birds, and reptiles and of the various species contained within these groups.[23] One may conclude, therefore, that his taxonomic skepticism was not as extreme as he wished it to be.

Buffon was not an unqualified advocate of the conception of a continuous and evenly graduated scale of natural entities. He did admit that "imperceptible nuances" were the "great work of nature" and that gaps between the different natural productions, the obvious places for taxonomic separation, seemed to be nonexistent. Nevertheless, the great chain of being became for Buffon a complex and highly interwoven network (*faisceau*) of organisms, each kind being separated not by precise and equal intervals but by divisions of many degrees and innumerable forms. The unique scale of organic nature, thought to ascend evenly from plant and polyp to mammal and man, was in reality branching, and the branches sometimes returned to join again at some new level. The scale was complex and not linear. In some ways this view is surprisingly similar to that held by Linnaeus. In place of an almost infinitely branched network, Linnaeus suggested the metaphor of a map: each species maintained fixed and well-demarcated relations with all those which surrounded it.[24] Both Linnaeus and Buffon were groping toward a truth which each in his own way suspected but which neither was to articulate fully. This was a recognition of the existence and meaning of the extraordinary intricacy with which organisms were adapted to the circumstances of their life. Linnaeus accounted for this nice adjustment of means to ends by calling attention to God's power and omniscience and His great concern for each of His creatures. Buffon explained the intricacies of animal organization by developing a theory of the relative value to the organism of the various organ systems, each major system calling forth a complex of lesser structures and patterns of behavior. This scheme was founded ultimately upon the Aristotelian zoological philosophy.

It was the writings of Buffon which first introduced Cuvier to the work of the Greek philosopher and zoologist. Like Buffon, Cuvier was to find in the Aristotelian biological corpus the general principles which he believed would lead to the erection of a new science of natural history. The principles, including the teleological conception of life, the notion of the unalterable functional integrity of the organism, and the idea of assigning various degrees of importance to the different organic functions, were those by which it was thought that natural history could acquire its own rationality and lawfulness, and hence could enter the sacred domain of Newtonian science.

Cuvier had known of the investigations of Buffon and Linnaeus from his earliest years. Their books had been his first masters in natural history. He related that the "taste for natural history" came to him while visiting a relative whose library contained a complete edition of Buffon. Cuvier studied the text and then colored the plates after Buffon's descriptions. He felt that these exercises had given him, at the age of 12, a more profound knowledge of the quadrupeds and birds than that possessed by the majority of older naturalists. Later, his botany teacher at Stuttgart, Kerner, made him a present of "a Linnaeus." This work, the tenth edition of the *Systema naturae*, remained his "companion and guide" during the "solitary studies" which characterized his residence in Normandy.[25] Cuvier acknowledged freely his debt to his predecessors but he was also fully cognizant of their limitations. The spiritual disciple of both Linnaeus and Buffon, as well as of the entire eighteenth-century development of natural history, Cuvier himself perhaps best expresesd the virtues and the shortcomings of his two masters. In the Prospectus to what was to become one of the basic handbooks of nineteenth-century natural history he declared:

Linnaeus grasped with finesse the distinctive traits of the organisms; Buffon embraced in a glance their most remote relationships. Linnaeus, exact and precise, invented a special language to present his ideas in all their rigor; Buffon, abundant and fecund, utilized all of his resources to develop the breadth of his conceptions. No one has ever more deeply felt the beauties of detail with which the Creator has endowed nature than Linnaeus; no one has ever painted the majesty of creation and the imposing grandeur of the laws to which it is subjected better than Buffon. The former, appalled by the chaos in which his predecessors had left the *histoire* of nature, sought, by simple means and short, to put order into this immense maze and to make the knowledge of individual creatures less difficult; the latter, repelled by the dryness of writers who, for the most part, were content to be exact, sought to arouse our interest in these particular creatures by the fascination of his harmonious and poetic language. Sometimes, wearied by the difficult study of Linnaeus, we find repose in Buffon; but always, when we have been pleasantly moved by his enchanting tableaux, we wish to return to Linnaeus so that we may place in order these charming impressions of which we possess only a confused recollection; and it is doubtless not the least merit of these two authors to inspire us to turn continuously from one to the other, although this alternative seems to prove and in fact does prove that something is lacking in each of them.[26]

Cuvier proposed, by the systematic development of natural history based upon well-founded and precise first principles, to eliminate this deficiency and to bring together in one complete body the taxonomic and philosophic elements of his science. The first element in the logic of the new system was a careful definition and, hence, interpretation of the word "nature." From his general conception of nature Cuvier carried the development of theoretical zoology toward an enunciation of the rules of comparative anatomy. The indispensable intermediate stage in this development was the formulation of the idea of the "conditions of existence," and it was here that the Aristotelian biological philosophy began to exert its influence.

II

Nature and the Conditions of Existence

Life is the most beautiful spectacle and the most difficult problem presented to the curiosity of man — CUVIER [1]

C UVIER's conception of nature suggested to him the ostensible rational explanation of animal form, a central problem of anatomical science. By postulating a lawful universe from which all chance occurrence was excluded, he was compelled to believe that the individual animal and the role which it played in the organic world were directly dependent, through the intermediation of the processes of the animal functions, upon the laws given to the physical world by its Creator. Cuvier's functionalism, the theoretical basis of his anatomical and zoological studies, was a restatement of the thorough-going teleological interpretation of life which he had adapted from Aristotle and from his French predecessors. The physiological expression of the directedness of vital processes was a characteristic mark of Cuvier's system of organic nature and it opened the path to the discovery of the structural bases and relative importance of the various animal functions.

A view of nature

Cuvier's single, brief statement of a general definition of nature appeared late in his scientific career (1825).[2] Whereas Linnaeus and especially Buffon had written frequently and eloquently upon the

26

subject, Cuvier had previously only incidentally presented his opinions. This essay of 1825 was not the result of purely peaceful reflection. It was a discretely polemical piece, another step in a barely submerged dispute with Etienne Geoffroy Saint-Hilaire which became notoriously public in the *débat* at the Académie des sciences during the spring of 1830. The dictionary article on nature was therefore an excellent platform from which to proclaim his doctrines and attempt to refute those of his colleague.

The essay opened with three negative definitions of nature. Cuvier was confident that the refutation of each permitted but one further interpretation, his own. The first error was to associate nature with *naissance*, birth. When applied to the world of animals, plants, and minerals this meaning of nature designated the qualities which these entities possess by virtue of birth or origin, in distinction to the attributes which they might have subsequently acquired by (man's) artifice. For example, man is by "nature" educable, he is "naturally" passionate, inconstant, and filled with anxiety. Gold is by "nature" a heavy, yellow, chemically inactive substance. The "nature" of an object was therefore merely the essence of that object, whether it was an individual animal, a species of plants, or the whole of creation. The second error, closely related to the first, was to take the nature of an object to be the object itself. Instead of qualities or attributes, "nature," Cuvier said, "now connotes the substances to which these qualities belong; nature is then the totality of creatures, or the universe, or the world . . . [or] creation: *nature*, the *world*, the *creation*, the *sum total of created beings* are then so many synonyms." But the final and most dangerous error was to personify nature. The existing creatures, the laws which govern their interrelations and maintain just proportion and order in the world, the pleasures experienced by sensitive beings, all appeared to demonstrate an independent intelligence and bounty in nature. "Here, evidently," Cuvier commented bitterly, "under the term *nature* the creator himself is portrayed."

The common fallacy of these definitions lay in their separation of nature from the Creator. Cuvier of course believed that nature was orderly and that the search for the characteristics and attributes of natural objects was the primary task of the natural historian. He was forever conscious that in every feature and in every mutation nature betrayed the intelligence and foresight with which she had been created. Orderliness, factual knowledge, or intelligibility were not in themselves sufficient indications of the essential aspect of nature. Nature was orderly because she was subject to the laws ordained by the Creator; our factual knowledge was useful to us and was also a means to glorify the Creator; and nature's intelligibility was nothing less than the direct product of the Creator's previsions.

As striking as the unoriginality of this viewpoint, certainly a common one at this period, was the rigor and moral conviction with which it was presented. Cuvier was careful to circumscribe precisely his idea of nature:

The word *nature* is thus only an abridged and rather ambiguous way of denoting the existing creatures and their associated phenomena. In considering these phenomena in regard to their immediate causes, and to their basic and universal cause, and if we assume that at least in everything which we can observe of these phenomena they depend upon the laws of motion, combined with forms which these bodies received at their origin, we see that the idea of *birth*, of beginning, which furnishes the root of the word, is preserved in more or less all of its usual acceptations, but we also see how puerile are the philosophers who have given nature a kind of individual existence, distinct from the creator, from the laws which he has imposed upon motion, and from the properties or forms which he has given to the creatures.[3]

The laws of motion were the best illustration of the rules decreed by the Creator for the conservation and harmony of the world. Nature, through these laws, stood immediately subjected to the will of the Creator. To say, therefore, that the "nature" of an object lay in its "qualities" was to ignore perversely the clear connection between the Creator and the universe, and to personify nature, identifying her with the Creator, was certainly the most pernicious possible turn in philosophy.

Cuvier's physical world, then, was a machine, its operations proceeding harmoniously under direction of the Creator's laws. Cuvier believed that the Creator, always immanent in nature and an omnipotent, wise, and good being, had promulgated these laws, probably at the moment of the creation, and that since the origin of the world He had only rarely acted on, or through the intermediation of, physical events. Nevertheless, the laws of nature, however simple they were assumed to be, did not compel nature herself to be simple. Quite to the contrary, Cuvier held that complexity and profusion of form were equally a part of nature. To the familiar axiom that everything must be accomplished in the simplest possible manner, Cuvier replied, in words recalling Buffon, that

it is far from being most simple to use the same materials for different aims and it is easy to think of cases where this method would be the most complicated of all and, furthermore, nothing is less proved than this constant simplicity of means. Beauty, richness, and abundance have been among the aims of the creator no less than simplicity.[4]

Cuvier understood nature to be "the production of omnipotence, ruled by a wisdom whose laws we discover only through observation." Cuvier's nature was certainly as intelligible as that of Linnaeus and as lawful as that of Buffon. It excluded an independent "boundless force" (Buffon), but it did remain, as it had been for both Linnaeus and Buffon, fascinating, multiform, and integrally whole. It was a conservative and static conception of nature and one which was certain to be attacked by the advocates of a more self-sufficient and dynamic view of the world.

Sciences and problems of life

Cuvier remarked that the laws of nature must be discovered. They were not self-evident to the untrained observer. As of so many other subjects, he frequently essayed classifications of the sciences, sometimes dividing them by their mathematical sophistication and other times by their subject matter and methods of study. His primary division rested ultimately upon the degree of quantification obtained by the science. "Mechanics," he declared, "has thus become an almost wholly mathematical science; chemistry remains a still strictly experimental science, while natural history has long been in many of its parts a science of observation alone." [5] This passage implies that increasing quantification is the ideal, as well as the distinctive character, of the physical and natural sciences. The ideal, unfortunately, could not always be taken for the fact, since control of the conditions of a phenomenon, a necessity for its precise delimitation, had not yet been realized in the natural sciences. But the naturalist need not despair, for Cuvier believed that natural history might yet discover its own rules whose rigor would equal that of the laws of mechanics although they would perhaps not be mathematical in form.

What is meant by the natural history of an object? It was, Cuvier replied, nothing other than the complete knowledge of that object. "I repeat," he said, "the natural history of any body whatsoever is the knowledge of all of its parts, as much internal as external, of its relationships with other beings, of all the phenomena of its existence, and of the causes of its existence." These requirements pass well beyond the simple identification and description of an animal or plant, commonly considered to be the task of natural history. Cuvier here follows Buffon and not Linnaeus: the behavior, the environmental relations, the physiology, and, above all, the "causes" of an animal were considered to be as important as its anatomy or taxonomic status. Cuvier's statement was a grand one, yet he would have been the first to declare the impossibility of any individual's uniting in himself all of the abilities necessary for the solution of these problems. He had once shown considerable interest in the minerals and had even delivered a general course in botany, but his own original researches were strictly confined to the animals, living and extinct. He was not a physiologist and his frequent essays on this subject were derived almost entirely from other sources. In the introduction to an unpublished series of lectures on comparative anatomy, pronounced about 1800, he presented the following idea of the "actual" and the "ideal" classifications of the natural-history sciences:

Ideal	Anatomy: structure of organic bodies
	Physiology: explanation of their phenomena
	Zoology: natural history of an animal
	Botany: natural history of a plant
Actual	Physiology: physicochemical explanation of organic phenomena
	Anatomy: description of internal parts
	Zoology: description of external animal parts
	Botany: description of external plant parts.

Cuvier, in both schemes, was an anatomist and a zoologist, but it is important to note that zoology in the "ideal" scheme meant the thorough study of the complete animal, an attempt to realize the definition of natural history given above. Cuvier was by his own definitions a zoologist and not a natural historian or a paleontologist. The term "biologist," unknown in his youth and not yet in universal currency during his lifetime, can be used with reference to Cuvier only as an acknowledged but sometimes useful anachronism.[6]

It is evident that the study of zoology, in Cuvier's opinion, necessitated a broad familiarity with the results, if not the practice, of physiology. He himself held very definite ideas on the nature of life, on the physicochemical explanations of its phenomena, and on the inherent limits set to man's exploration of the subject. To identify precisely the sources upon which he relied for his physiological information would be, however, an exceedingly difficult and probably thankless task. It would require listing almost every physiological treatise published during the eighteenth and early nineteenth centuries, as perhaps few men have ever read so widely and so thoroughly in the sciences. One previous author, nevertheless, doubtless equally well read in his time, commanded Cuvier's special attention; this was Albrecht von Haller (1708–1777). Haller's unique abilities were once reviewed by Cuvier (IFFC 97) for his audience at the Collège de France; erudition, scorn for systematizers, patient observation, rigorous and elegant descriptions, excellent individual anatomies, the constant use of comparative anatomy, and the determination of the vital forces were listed as the marks of Haller's genius. His distinction between irritability and sensibility proved useful in Cuvier's presentation of basic animal structure, and the Swiss physiologist's numerous works served Cuvier and others as an enormous mine of physiological learning. Cuvier also gave his approval to the physiological researches of A. L. de Lavoisier and P. S. de Laplace, the *abbé* L. Spallanzani, and L. Galvani.

For Cuvier the animal organism was a dynamic unity which, in constant interaction with a changing environment, maintained its integrity and preserved its form and was capable of transmitting these capacities to its offspring. Life seemed to be a directed flux of matter whose ceaseless motion was discovered by the chemical, anatomical, and physiological study of the organic body. In 1810 he ventured the following characterization of life:

> In living bodies each part has its special and distinct composition; none of their molecules remains in place, everything successively enters and departs: life is a continuous whirlpool whose direction, complicated though it is, remains constant, as does the kind of molecules, but not the individual molecules themselves which are caught up in it; to the contrary, the present material of the living body will soon no longer be there and yet it [the body] is nevertheless the depository of the force which will constrain future material to follow the same path.[7]

The appeal to these molecules, forming as they did the material basis of the solid framework of the body and of organic chemical phenomena, reveals the influence on Cuvier of eighteenth-century physiological thought.

There existed in later eighteenth-century physiology a significant trend toward "iatrochemism," an attempt to explain all vital processes in chemical terms. The chemical model which was beginning to replace the earlier mechanical models (for example, the Boer-haavian solids and fluids) was in part another product of the quest for lawfulness arising from the successes of the Cartesian and Newtonian systems. It was often not difficult to demonstrate the inadequacy, or inaccuracy, of a mechanical explanation of vital processes. The discovery, for example, of the major roles played by the gastric juice and stomach acid in digestion, leading to a relative devaluation of mechanical digestive resources (mastication, trituration, and so forth), illustrates this point. Physiology, rapidly becoming an experimental science, began also to recognize certain peculiar requirements of its subject matter. It was now clear to some physiologists that experimental analysis, the resolution of a physiological problem into its component parts, might lead to the death of the experimental animal and hence to the disappearance of the very phenomena that it had been desired to study.[8]

Physiology also needed to explain the so-called wholeness of the organism. It scarcely seemed possible that the animal, now viewed as an extremely complex system of particles and fluids only rarely in a fixed state and among which occurred the essential changes of the body, could continue to exist directed only by the seemingly capricious and destructive action of physical forces. Some special integrative force, controlling the other forces and assuring the unity of the organism, appeared to many physiologists to be a necessary feature of the living creature. Partly in answer to this demand appeared a tradition of moderate vitalism which, from G. F. Stahl through the school of Montpellier to Cuvier's contemporary, X. Bichat, provided a conceptual framework and even an experimental guide for those who feared ill consequences from overmanipulation of the living organism. Whatever may have been the virtues or defects of this movement, rejuvenated vitalism does seem to have helped force the physiologist and the zoologist to examine the organism as a whole, to treat the totality of its properties and processes. Cuvier certainly enough rejected any form of vitalism but his eclectic physiological doctrine accepted as its primary principle the wholeness of the organism. The vital processes underlying organic wholeness remained, however, the effect of both chemical and mechanical action, neither of these theories completely winning his sympathies.

The chemical viewpoint had received a powerful stimulus from the publication of the memoirs and the *Traité élémentaire de chimie* (1789) by Lavoisier. Cuvier immediately recognized the importance of the new chemical system and the researches upon which it was based. As early as February 1790 he addressed a long review of the *Traité* to his friend Pfaff, in which the latter, a proponent of the phlogiston theory of chemical reaction, was urged to procure quickly this example of "unsurpassed chemistry" which based all knowledge upon "calculation and experiments" and contained neither "hypotheses nor vague demonstrations." It appeared that chemistry had adopted the mathematical spirit. Not the least exciting of the results of the laboratory analyses of the geometer-chemists, Cuvier believed, was the revelation of the chemical simplicity of life. Carbon, hydrogen, oxygen, and nitrogen, plus a few traces of other elements, constituted the chemical basis of life. He confidently indulged his optimism by declaring that

there emerges from all these facts some even more important results which bring us to a general theory of organized beings and which reveal for us the essence of life itself in the perpetual variations of the rather few [constituent] elements. A little oxygen and some nitrogen, there is, in the present state of science, the only apparent cause of the innumerable products of organic bodies.

It is evident from these words that chemistry, in spite of its great advances, remained for Cuvier essentially a catalogue of the elements and a synopsis of their combinations. Chemistry, as might have been expected, presented the building blocks of the organism and this was considered sufficient.[9]

There was one genus of chemical reaction, however, which attracted Cuvier's attention because of its direct relevance to vital processes. This was combustion. The chemistry of combustion,

34

worked out over several decades by Lavoisier, Laplace, and others, had led to the identification of animal respiration with the oxidation of carbon within the animal body. Respiration, which Cuvier considered (after sensation and movement) the most obviously "animal" function, found in combustion, which in turn "precedes, accompanies, or constitutes the majority of chemical operations and vital functions," an accurate and what appeared to be an essentially complete explanation. There remained in Cuvier's thinking and in that of many of his contemporaries considerable confusion about the exact location within the body of the various respiratory activities (gas exchange and production of animal heat). These perplexities may be passed over here, yet it is important to understand the use which Cuvier made of combustion chemistry. It is clear that he was especially interested in gross physiology, in respiration, nutrition, and so on, and considerably less concerned with various individual chemical processes in the body. The vital *tourbillon* in which the particles, composed of a few elements or simple compounds, circulated, separated, and reunited was a convenient and superficially satisfying explanation of life. But even more tangible, Cuvier believed, were the phenomena of combustion and respiration and these had the further merit of often being obviously and directly related to specific organic structures, for example, the lungs, heart, and circulatory vessels. Cuvier's chemical physiology was therefore an amalgam of a firmly disciplined corpuscular mechanism and a moderately sophisticated adaptation of the new combustion chemistry. This system was perhaps neither better nor worse than those of other nonphysiologists. It was simply a wholly derivative system for which Cuvier never claimed more than being abreast with contemporary science.[10]

Conclusive as these mechanicochemical ideas may have appeared, they did not persuade Cuvier that the physiological problem of life had been solved. Life itself remained inexplicable. It seemed to be nothing more than the sum total of the phenomena observed in an organism. Early in his career he had said that the idea of life is one of those general and obscure ideas induced in us by certain sequences of phenomena which we see follow one another and which preserve their mutual relationships. Although we are ignorant of the link which unites them, we feel that this connection must exist and that is sufficient for us to designate them by a name commonly regarded as a sign of a particular principle, although in fact this may never represent anything more than the *ensemble* of phenomena.[11]

These words, one suspects, suggest less a cautious skepticism than they directly attack vitalistic explanations. Already it has been seen that Cuvier discarded vitalistic "special forces," and the tone of his criticism can be ascertained from a passage written in 1827: "the vital principle, that other kind of soul [that is, different from the divine human soul], which is neither material nor spiritual, and upon which is laid all that which cannot otherwise be explained, has moved off into the realm of chimeras." His objections were partially directed against the implausibility or impossibility of the existence, or of the effectiveness, of the "other kind of soul" but even more did they attack the experimental fruitlessness and explanatory emptiness of vitalist philosophy. Thus, in 1807, he argued that there can be only two kinds of explanations in the sciences, the physical and the nonphysical. When our ideal explanation (the physical) fails, we should turn not to speculation but to experimentation. To propose a vital force is "ridiculous, meaningless," and defeatist. One must follow the example of physics and, just as Newton analyzed the problem of attraction into its individual instances, so must the physiologist remove the complexities from his problems. Cuvier developed this argument by contrasting the ideas and work of Haller and of P. J. Barthez (1734–1806), *montpellérain*, physician to Louis XVI and Napoleon I, and a prominent theoretician of vitalist physiology. Haller's memoir of 1756 had shown how so-called vital forces could be reduced to the experimentally meaningful concepts of irritability and sensibility. Barthez, Cuvier felt, had followed a reactionary course and refused to admit his ignorance. Discontented by the limited range of physicochemical explanation, he constructed a physiology not of facts but of ideas, essential to which was a central vital force affecting all parts of the body, nourishing these parts, producing the embryo, giving heat to the humors and so on. Consummate vanity and absurdity, Cuvier must have thought. The physiologist gained nothing from vague hypotheses, since chemistry, anatomy, and experimentation alone could lead to positive and therefore useful results. Experimentation, from this point of view, might indeed involve the destruction of life, yet it remained the only sure method of gaining valid knowledge of organic processes. It meant, above all, the complete renunciation of attempts to form a unitary explanation of life.[12]

The basis of Cuvier's ideas on generation was similar to that of his attitude toward vitalism. Generation, and particularly spontaneous generation, became crucial questions when he considered the problem of the transformation of biological species (see below, Chapter VI). It is convenient to provide here only a very brief sketch of his ideas on the origin and transmission of life. The former question posed no dilemma. The origin of life, Cuvier believed, had always remained hidden from man. Whenever man penetrated back, within the limits of his instruments and techniques, to the earliest stage in the life of an animal, he always discovered that the creature already lived. His search never betrayed the moment or stage at which life entered the organism. The question of the origin of life could not, therefore, be an empirical question and, like the issue of vitalism, should be left in the "realm of chimeras." Cuvier, who was a decided preformationist, unequivocally supported a generalization of these facts, remarking that "in the present state of things, life comes only from life and there exist no other [creatures] than those which have been transmitted from living body to living body in an uninterrupted succession." He thus rejected spontaneous generation and believed in reproductive continuity, and both ostensibly because the appearance of an organism not arising directly from a prior relative could not be observed.[13]

Functionalism and teleology

Why, it may be asked, should a zoologist such as Cuvier be so profoundly concerned with physiological questions? What interest could an anatomist have in the chemical, mechanical, and functional bases of life? The answer is found in Cuvier's definition of a zoologist, a scientist who demanded the fullest possible explanations of the greatest possible number of organic phenomena. It was commonly understood that success in this venture required the cooperation of each separate zoological discipline, of which anatomy and physiology were of primary interest and importance. Cooperation between these two disciplines was particularly important. Anatomy, isolated from general physiology, became merely a special exercise in clever manipulation and exhaustive description and failed to broaden one's understanding of the vital activities of the organism. Physiology, on the other hand, divorced from knowledge of the body parts which actually performed the operations of life, searched blindly in a peculiar kind of void. One learned about the mechanicochemical processes but remained ignorant of the complex total activity of the organism which was naturally associated with an organized body. This distinction, given here with perhaps excessive sharpness, nevertheless represents a popular and significant dichotomy in the viewpoint of anatomical zoology, a dichotomy from which arose two dominant morphological traditions, the functional and the formal.[14]

Functional anatomy takes as its starting point the activity of the organism. It concentrates upon the use for which the parts are destined and it tends to respect the wholeness of the organism. Formal anatomy is directed toward the static, structural arrangement of the animal. An individual part, removed from the living animal, still retains for the formalist all of its meaningfulness. An example illustrates this difference. To the functionalist the forelimb of the quadruped is an organ for swimming, flying, and walking and its structure is ingeniously adapted in size, arrangement, and flexibility to fulfill best the functions appropriate to its nature. To the formalist the forelimb is an intricate and amazing machine constructed of bone, muscle, nerve, and tendon. Only incidentally does it seem to serve for functions such as walking or swimming. The pure anatomist is satisfied to know well the structural units of the body; the functional anatomist finds these units of interest only insofar as they are illustrative of the operations of the animal economy.

The functional viewpoint is among the most ancient biological generalizations. Probably its first statement appeared in Aristotle's *Parts of animals* (645 b; transl. A. E. Peck):

> Now, as each of the parts of the body, like every other instrument, is for the sake of some purpose, viz., some action, it is evident that the body as a whole must exist for the sake of some complex action. Just as the saw is there for the sake of sawing and not sawing for the sake of the saw, because sawing is the using of the instrument, so in some way the body exists for the sake of the soul, and the parts of the body for the sake of those functions to which they are naturally adapted.

Aristotle's influence upon Cuvier has already been emphasized. Cuvier was well aware of the importance of Aristotle's views for his own investigations. While still in Normandy he wrote to his friend Pfaff that he admired the treatises on the *History of animals* and the *Parts of animals* more each time he reread them and that it was Aristotle's works which were the "first essay in scientific natural history." [15] This influence became most explicit, however, as Cuvier attempted to fulfill one of his highest ambitions, the establishment of a definitive theory of functional anatomy.

In his mind the new theory would mean a necessarily rational anatomy. The disparate scattered facts of anatomical practice would be gathered together and thus would be born a new system of uncontested generality and unprecedented veracity. It appeared that even anatomy, that arid science of seemingly random facts, could be reduced to a small number of simple and precise laws and hence attain almost mathematical strictness. Cuvier's own anatomical theory was founded upon the hypothesis of the "conditions of existence." These conditions, logically prior to the existence of the organism and stated in functional terms, determined the basic physical organization of the animal. Cuvier believed that they were a teleological device whose certainty permitted the zoologist, now that he possessed a general statement of the nature of the organism, actually to predict the body structures which this creature must necessarily exhibit.

In a teleological system future ends are offered in explanation of present phenomena. However obscure the link between the ends and events may be, the system must assume that this connection is firm and that the ends are realized in a definite and orderly manner. Biology, with its countless instances of means nicely adjusted to ends, has naturally always sheltered some form of teleological thinking.[16] Aristotle fathered the teleological school, and in more modern times, while in the physical sciences attempts were made to break away from this philosophy, many noted naturalists, among them John Ray, Andreas Cesalpino, Linnaeus, and Cuvier, continued to use it and labored to demonstrate its ultimate truth. Their task was made easier and their arguments apparently more convincing because nature does in fact appear to be purposeful. The contemporary paleontologist G. G. Simpson, certainly no teleologist, has suggested that

this appearance of purposefulness is pervading in nature, in the general structure of animals and plants, in the mechanisms of their various organs, and in the give and take of their relationships with each other. Accounting for this apparent purposefulness is a basic problem for any system of philosophy or of science.[17]

In modern times the biological resolution of the problem of plan and purpose in nature is sought in the processes of organic evolution. Purposefulness is considered to be merely apparent and may be thought to result from an inadequate analysis of that crucial issue in evolutionary theory, biological adaptation. One scarcely need emphasize how foreign and repugnant this argument would have appeared to a mind with Cuvier's preconceptions. The seemingly incredible sequence of unlikely coincidences necessary to produce, for example, the opposable thumb to which man owes his extraordinary manual dexterity would repel the teleologist as nothing else might. Not blind chance, but the operation of the final cause of this hand had brought it into being. Man, together with certain simians, possesses unique mental abilities, and needs just such an instrument for the execution of his desires, and hence he has been endowed with this versatile organ.

Aristotelian philosophy presented the teleological system as primarily a philosophical and not a religious doctrine, that is, it portrayed a universe whose inherent finality did not depend upon a unique, historical, creative act performed by an eternal author. Later, of course, Christian apologetics used the apparent finality of nature as evidence of the bounty and intelligence of God and as proof of His existence. The Aristotelian teleology, uncorrupted by the design argument, derived from the Platonic Idea of the Good. Although the Idea of the Good could direct "cosmical processes by its mere presence," Logan argues that the Platonic Ideal was in fact too remote from the terrestrial world to be a genuinely effective cause of physical events.[18] Aristotle's system, on the other hand, offered a more fully developed teleology in which the purpose or final cause of a phenomenon was not sharply separated from the means of its realization. They were considered to be mutually necessary. They furthermore implied the two essential biological causes: the final cause, which established the nature of an organism and hence its form, and the material cause, the physical substance from which the organism was constructed. To Aristotle and, later, to Cuvier it seemed absurd to postulate the final cause of an organism without also providing the means by which it could be fulfilled. Aristotle further proclaimed, as the passage from the *Parts of animals* reveals, that every individual or species of animal possessed its unique *raison d'être* and that each part of an organism participated together with all of the other parts in the manifestation of this end. Each individual or species possessed its own immanent entelechy which constantly sought to attain the absolute entelechy.

Cuvier, primarily a zoologist and never really concerned with the formal discussion of teleological thought, naturally disregarded the aging and elaborate philosophical basis of the Aristotelian argument. Of no concern to him were the complexities of the hierarchy of causes or the relations of the various entelechies to the absolute entelechy. What was important to him in the Aristotelian system, in addition to its general teleological trend, was the refusal to separate categorically the physical structure and mechanism of the organic body from their teleological explanation. It is interesting to note that he was either unaware of or rejected the recent criticism brought to the teleological argument by Kant. Kant had considered the two levels of purposefulness in nature: the universe as a whole and the individuals within it.[19] His major criticism, and the one from which Cuvier drew no profit, stated that teleological explanations were wholly creations of the reflective judgment and may be used only as heuristic devices. Since pure mechanism had failed to resolve the fundamental biological problems, the naturalist was permitted to think of nature *as if* she were end-directed. Whether or not nature was actually the product of prior purpose was an unanswerable question. Kant's cautious conclusion still influences thinking on the teleological problem, but it had absolutely no influence on Cuvier. Cuvier's theoretical biology was based upon teleological reasoning in its most literal form. He preached it publicly, he adopted it in practice, and he never abandoned it. Its clearest and most forceful statement appears in the Introduction to the *Règne animal*:

> Natural history nevertheless has a rational principle that is exclusive to it and which it employs with great advantage on many occasions; it is the *conditions of existence* or, popularly, *final causes*. As nothing may exist which does not include the conditions which made its existence possible, the different parts of each creature must be coordinated in such a way as to make possible the whole organism, not only in itself but in its relationship to those which surround it, and the analysis of these conditions often leads to general laws as well founded as those of calculation or experiment.[20]

Cuvier's words are almost a paraphrase of those of Aristotle. Let it be repeated, Cuvier was a teleologist in a most literal manner. He did not utter these words merely because he sought theoretical completeness or philosophical elegance. For example, while engaged during the last years of his life in an acrimonious squabble over what might be the proper principles of anatomy, the worst he could say of his opponent (Etienne Geoffroy Saint-Hilaire) was that when the latter's ideas were novel, they were in error, and when they were correct, they had already been stated by Aristotle! At the center of this debate over general principles was the question of whether abstract and almost wholly morphological conceptions should be supreme in zoology (Geoffroy) or whether the essence of the animal and its structure was really to be found in the functional integration and correlation of all of the constituent parts. Cuvier naturally favored the latter point of view, and he was proud to say that the source of his wisdom was Aristotle.[21]

In summary, Cuvier believed that among the (biological) laws with which nature had been endowed at the creation were the conditions of existence, principles which stated the fundamental characteristics of each and every creature. The primary feature of any organism was its functional unity, a unity resulting from the coordination of the parts of the organism and their subordinate physico-chemical processes. The connection between the conditions of existence, the abstract essence of the animal, usually stated in functional terms, and the coordination of the body structures, the tangible realization of the conditions of existence, provided him with the theoretical foundations of natural history. Henceforth known as the "correlation of parts," this connection led to the emergence of a new science of anatomy. Anatomy became functional and comparative and its procedures and discoveries were soon passing, in Cuvier's hands, from strictly morphological science to the classification of animals and the reconstruction of fossil quadrupeds. The correlation of parts was the first anatomical rule and thus the focal point for all of Cuvier's subsequent zoological investigations.

43

III

Comparative Anatomy

*I admired in your Comparative Anatomy
the wealth of information and its manner
of presentation . . . You have broken a
new trail, you have taken the giant's step.*
— A. G. CAMPER [1]

THE demonstration of the connection between the conditions of existence and the anatomical rules, once the latter had been distinguished from their original abstract formulation in teleological terms, became an essentially anatomical problem. Descriptive anatomy was merely the first step in Cuvier's creation of a new anatomical science. The raw data obtained by dissection and observation had to be generalized by comparison and then interpreted by the application of the principle of correlation of parts. In this process the rules for descriptive anatomy were established and man's physical structure, which had long been considered representative of that of all other vertebrate animals, was found to occupy no supreme or even major place in the animate world. There thus emerged as a result of Cuvier's researches a revivified science of anatomy, a science now believed to be at once particular and general, empirical and rational. The ancient science of anatomy had indeed been set in new directions.

Anatomical observation is perhaps as old as scientific investiga-

44

tion itself. From Roman antiquity and the studies of Galen, anatomy had meant primarily medical anatomy. Owing probably to the difficulty of obtaining human material for dissection, medical anatomists were compelled to use bodies of animals for the explication of human structure, a situation which persisted until and even after the anatomical renaissance in the sixteenth-century Italian universities. In the following century animal anatomy continued to contribute primarily to the advance of medicine and human physiology. Harvey's observations of the motion of the heart in various animals and the discovery by Aselli of the lactic vessels of the dog were the work of physicians. Detailed studies of the special structures of the human body were also pursued so that by 1750 medical anatomy could be considered reasonably complete except for general microstructure and the internal organization of certain parts. Animal anatomy, or, in eighteenth-century terminology, zootomy, had not been equally successful. Exhaustive memoirs on some species, for example, the horse, were available before the eighteenth century and Claude Perrault, physician and architect to Louis XIV, had published in the 1670's several significant memoirs on the lion, turtle, monkey, eagle, and others. Unquestionably the anatomical facts relating to common vertebrates had greatly increased by 1750, but this achievement was easily outweighed by the general and profound ignorance which prevailed of the structure, if not the very existence, of the more exotic vertebrates and of almost all of the invertebrate animals. Invertebrate anatomy had of course been the subject of several important studies, among them those of Malphigi, Swammerdam, Leeuwenhoek, Vallisnieri, and especially Réaumur. These specialized monographs, however, did not permit the creation of an independent science of animal anatomy. Furthermore, few if any systematic anatomies of complete series of different animals existed. The invertebrates in particular were subject to the whims of curiosity of even those few who recognized their interest and significance. The marine invertebrates, so much more diverse than the terrestrial and aquatic forms, were almost completely un-

45

known. Cuvier might correctly have boasted that his studies on the marine fauna literally continued the work of Aristotle.

Another problem was that the study of the vertebrates had placed first importance upon external appearance and structure while neglecting internal anatomy. This neglect appears to have been deliberate. L. J. M. Daubenton, Buffon's collaborator and an exceptionally talented anatomist, wrote in 1753 that he would confine himself to examining the "principal parts" and regard only the visceral organs, lungs, stomach, and so on. The muscles, nerves, arteries, and veins were neglected simply because they were deemed to have little importance in the animal economy.[2] It is as important to recognize these continuing gaps in anatomical knowledge as it is to emphasize the very great advances of this science during the eighteenth century, since a corollary of the ever-increasing amount of information was the persistent lack of general conclusions.

The formulation of functional anatomy

Cuvier, perhaps more than any other zoologist, was instrumental in the creation of a new, rationally ordered science of anatomy, but the initial inspiration and fundamental principles of the new anatomy had originally been the property of another, now forgotten anatomist, Félix Vicq-d'Azyr. Born in 1748 in Valognes (Manche), the son of a physician, Vicq-d'Azyr had studied letters and philosophy at the university in Caen.[3] He arrived in Paris shortly after the termination of the Seven Years' War and continued there his studies in anatomy and physiology in preparation for a medical career. Successful in practice, he also found time to assist A. Petit and Daubenton in their anatomical investigations. He was elected to the Académie des sciences in 1774 and was appointed by Turgot the first *secrétaire perpétuel* of the newly founded (1776) Société royale de médecine, an assembly especially concerned with the problems of public health and constantly under attack by the older and privileged Académie de médecine. In 1788 he received Buffon's chair at the Académie Française. The revolution reversed his fortunes. As private physician to Marie Antoinette and the comte d'Artois, the future Charles X, Vicq-d'Azyr during the Terror fervently devoted himself to his practice, teaching, and research, probably hoping to be overlooked. He was not forgotten and Cuvier seriously relates the story that he died from the strain of celebrating the *fête* of the Supreme Being in June 1794, at which his attendance was reportedly demanded by Robespierre himself. However this may be (he had long shown symptoms of lung disease), his early death interrupted an already fruitful and still promising career.

Throughout his life, Vicq-d'Azyr had been concerned with the problems of vertebrate anatomy. His first major contributions, on the anatomy of the fish and the comparative structure of man and the birds, appeared in 1773. The following year he published a novel essay on the serial analogies between the four appendages of the quadruped animals. During the following two decades he prepared numerous studies on the organs of hearing, on those of voice, on the bones of the shoulder, and on avian eggs and generation. His greatest interest was the vertebrate nervous system. After a memoir on the second and third cranial nerve pairs, he published (1781) four large reports on the brain, spinal cord, and associated nerve origins. These were but a preliminary statement and were followed in 1786 by his first major anatomical work, the *Traité d'anatomie et physiologie*, a detailed and illustrated account of the encephalon but of no other parts. In 1792 appeared volume two (volume one was never written) of his contribution to the vast *Encyclopédie méthodique*, the *Système anatomique des quadrupèdes*. The work was finally completed in four volumes, considerably altered from their original conception, by H. Cloquet in 1822.

Apart from this enormous mass of factual information, Vicq-d'Azyr's work presented a deliberate innovation in anatomical practice. Recalling how Daubenton had concentrated on the "general and external form of the skeleton and larger [parts]," he pointed out that anatomy was also the study of "articulations, ligaments, muscles, vessels, nerves, glands, [and] the internal structure of the

47

viscera," and that these parts must be studied in each animal. The previously cited memoirs contain the results of this procedure, a work of "immense difficulties," as Vicq-d'Azyr himself realized. It meant a more refined technique in dissection, the patient tracing of small and often obscure structures, and the collection of similar data, presented in similar terms, gathered from the most dissimilar animals. In the course of assembling these data he retained the age-old model for anatomical research, man. Being both a physician and an anatomist he could not reject his most familiar and physically and morally most important subject. He appears to have remained undecided about the exact role which human structure might play in anatomical research. Man's real importance, he believed, lay in his relationship to the animals: apart from man animal structure meant nothing, and man without the animals appeared less imposing than he really is. Man, he concluded, must be the first organism treated, because of his innate interest for us and because of the great importance in nature of his activity.[4]

Vicq-d'Azyr's primary goal was neither the mere elucidation of the heretofore little-known internal animal organization nor just another study of the human body. He sought to uncover the total relationships of all animals, including man, and to discover and expose their common features. To succeed in this desire the rigorous use of the comparative method was necessary and, if Vicq-d'Azyr is remembered for nothing else, certainly his demands for the use of comparison as the basis of anatomy deserve to be recalled. Cuvier, the so-called *fondateur* of comparative anatomy, owed far more to his predecessor than is usually admitted. The comparison of the totality of characters of all animals being a patently impossible task, should they in fact have all been identified and described (which was in no way true), some system of selection was essential for anatomical progress. Vicq-d'Azyr's response was to select the characters on physiological grounds. "Anatomy, taken by itself," he said, "is, so to speak, only the skeleton of science; it is physiology which animates it. The one is the study of life; the other is only the study of death." In order to unite human and comparative anatomy and theoretical and experimental physiology and make all "concur toward the same goal," he proposed following successively the vital functions and then the organs which subserved them. The function (for example, digestion) would first be defined, then would come the presentation of the organ system performing it, followed in turn by complete descriptions of the individual organs and a review of the appearance or nonappearance of these parts in the different animal species. Although Vicq-d'Azyr never prepared a complete account of the animals which fulfilled these demands, he did present a lengthy and detailed *précis* of what the system would require and how it might be organized ("Tableau d'un cours d'anatomie et physiologie"). Here are listed the nine special animal functions: ossification, irritability, circulation, sensibility, respiration, digestion, secretion, generation, and nutrition, all related to the three general animal functions: nutrition, movement, and sensation. Under each special function he assembled a list of the parts and of their peculiarities, unresolved problems, references to the literature, and other items which would serve in the definitive formulation. Two similar lists appear in the same volume. In one the order is as follows: digestion, nutrition, circulation, respiration, secretion, ossification, generation, irritability, and sensibility ("Tableau des fonctions ou caractères propres aux corps vivants"). In the other, the list is arranged by the organs themselves and the functions must be inferred from these: stomach, intestines, external organ for aqueous respiration, visceral organs–lymph vessels–generative organs–nerve net, blood vessels–organs of vision, and so forth ("Tableau des animaux dans l'ordre de leur composition anatomique").[5]

Vicq-d'Azyr created an indissoluble bond between anatomy and physiology. This was a conception which, in itself, already possessed great antiquity but it was also an idea which had never before received such direct and thorough anatomical support. As has been seen, the physiological approach to anatomy was the foundation of Cuvier's anatomical studies and one can trace this seminal idea to

Aristotle or to Buffon, or to Vicq-d'Azyr. Cuvier accepted Vicq-d'Azyr's resolution of life into a small number of vital functions, but comparison of the lists reproduced above reveals a peculiarity which he could not accept: the order in which the functions are presented is never exactly the same. Respiration, for example, appears in fifth position on the first list, fourth on the second, and, seemingly, third on the third list. In one case it precedes digestion, in another case secretion, and on the third list a whole medley of functions. This arrangement or, rather, lack of arrangement reappears throughout Vicq-d'Azyr's anatomical writings, probably for the simple reason that an orderly hierarchy of functions did not seem evident or necessary to him. By contrast, the second Cuverian anatomical rule, the subordination of characters, may be considered as the epitome of the hierarchical arrangement of functions and therefore of organs. On this point the two anatomical systems differ profoundly, but do not stand in opposition. It may in fact be true that Cuvier's conception was scarcely more than the obvious termination of Vicq-d'Azyr's innovation.

It is not difficult to document Cuvier's debt to his able predecessor. How well informed he was of Vicq-d'Azyr's writings is clear from the manuscript copy and notes of the "Leçons d'anatomie comparée" (MHN 609, *prem. partie*). This large work is divided into chapter envelopes, each dealing with a separate organ or system, included in each of which are literally hundreds of small paper strips bearing some particular fact. The overwhelming majority of these strips cite as their source either Daubenton or Vicq-d'Azyr, the latter in greatest frequency. Like all anatomists, Cuvier wanted to draw as much of his information as possible from reliable authors and this manuscript indicates that he found none more dependable nor more useful than Vicq-d'Azyr. Apparently even before the preparation of this manuscript he had studied the work of Vicq-d'Azyr. In a closely written, thirty-page *cahier* included among the notes from several anatomies performed in Normandy, Cuvier methodically catalogued, following Vicq-d'Azyr's memoirs published by the Académie des sciences, the complete musculature of nine "families" of birds (MHN 609, *prem. partie*). It was nevertheless sad for Cuvier to contemplate this great factual wealth, for he had also recognized in Vicq-d'Azyr a mind which wished to generalize and to extend itself to the broadest anatomical conclusions. Preserved in the manuscript of the fourth lecture on comparative anatomy delivered in 1795 is a brief, four-page note in Cuvier's hand which reveals more clearly than all indirect evidence his estimation of the anatomist dead but a year previously. After proudly emphasizing the factual basis of contemporary anatomy he complains that it has remained without order and asks, where is the man who can bring order to this science?

A single man perhaps would have been able to give comparative anatomy the stimulus which would have made it advance rapidly toward perfection, but the sciences and society have lost him. There is no need for me to recall sorrowfully to you the illustrious Vicq-d'Azyr; this is not the place to cast flowers on his grave. Let us merely observe that his premature death is so much more unfortunate for the science which interests us because, too modest, too timid perhaps, feeling less than his readers the strength of his genius, he was often content to gather the facts without daring to deduce the results which he perceived more clearly than anyone else but of which, also more acutely than anyone, [he] perceived the weak sides and the obscure or doubtful points. The continuation of his work would have clarified these issues, removed these doubts, answered the objections; he would have meaningfully finished his sketch begun with so much boldness. But who today would dare to put his hand on this work; who would be rash enough to bring the brush to features drawn by Apelles? [6]

Cuvier, as it turned out, was himself the man whose boldness would remake the science, but only by following Vicq-d'Azyr's example.

Cuvier and descriptive anatomy

The first edition of Cuvier's major anatomical study, the *Leçons d'anatomie comparée*, began to appear but five years after the author had assumed the burdens of Mertrud's course at the Muséum. The first two volumes of Cuvier's lectures on comparative anatomy were collected and edited by A. M. C. Duméril, then director of anatomical work at the Faculté de Médecine and later a professor at the Faculté (1801) and at the Muséum (1825). For the final three volumes a similar task was performed by G. L. Duvernoy, physician and naturalist from Cuvier's native Montbéliard and destined to receive, via the Faculté des Sciences at Strasbourg, Cuvier's chair of natural history at the Collège de France.[7] In 1806 Cuvier lectured on anatomy at the Collège de France (IFFC 102) and in 1807 he began a very important series of lectures on the organs of sense and movement, continued in 1809, and terminated in 1812 (IFFC 104, 105). During this period he steadily produced memoirs on anatomical subjects, for example, a demonstration of the red blood of the leech (and hence the difficulties of the zoological category *animaux à sang blanc*, meaning the invertebrates), an analysis of the organs of voice in birds, and later a collected edition of his numerous memoirs on marine animals. After 1812 one encounters little exclusively anatomical research. Cuvier's interests had turned first to the preparation of the *Règne animal* and then to his great study of the fishes.

An unprecedented number of animals had been examined in the preparation of the *Leçons* and Cuvier was careful to declare his preference for actual observation to blind reliance upon previous authors. He did admit that the latter practice, although unfortunate, was frequently necessary. His intensive and detailed anatomical researches had begun in Normandy. In a letter to a Württemberg friend, Hartmann, written from Caen in 1790, he lists descriptions already made: 420 species [!] of *coquilles de mer*, 110 species of fishes, 11 species of amphibious quadrupeds, 14 species of sea urchins, 18 species of corals, and 30 species of exotic butterflies.[8] After 1792, when the d'Héricy family had sought a greater measure of personal security by moving from the city to their isolated country estate at Fiquainville, Cuvier no longer had access to the several natural history collections which he had employed at Caen and he turned to the direct study of marine species and the intensive investigation of common vertebrates. Five substantial notebooks from 1792 detail the visceral anatomy of the cat, mole, rat, rabbit, and mouse (MHN 608). They include general descriptions of organ arrangement, of selected organs and sometimes their internal anatomy, of the digestive tract, and of the circulatory vessels, which are recorded in red ink. A second series of similar notebooks describes the musculature of the heron, crow, duck, buzzard, cat, and others (MHN, 609, *prem. partie*).

These early descriptions suggest the breadth of the factual basis of the new anatomy. The *Leçons* themselves confirm the extent of the revolution which Cuvier effected in anatomical science. His lectures first consider (and here is seen the influence of eighteenth-century anatomy) the structure of man. They pass immediately, however, to the other quadrupeds (mammals, birds, reptiles), then to the different divisions of the mollusks, the crustacea, the larval and adult stages of the insects, the *vers*, and finally the *zoophytes* (see Chapter IV). An exhaustive description of each of these animals, had it been possible to achieve, would have given birth to an almost unlimited number of volumes. Cuvier avoided this problem in two ways: by limiting the degree of anatomical resolution of each animal and by using comparative exposition.

The *Leçons d'anatomie comparée* comprise five stout octavo volumes of text; nine large synoptic classificatory tables are appended to the first volume; and fifty-two small engraved plates are included in the final volume. The aim throughout the work was precise description of the parts, based on direct observation and clear nomenclature. Internal anatomy was deliberately emphasized, since, Cuvier remarked, "this anatomy is indispensable for the study of animals, where the most important organs are located within." [9] An example from the fourth volume of the *Leçons* dealing with the respiratory and circulatory systems demonstrates Cuvier's practice of internal anatomies. After discussing the principal elements of the invertebrate circulatory system and then reviewing in detail those of the

53

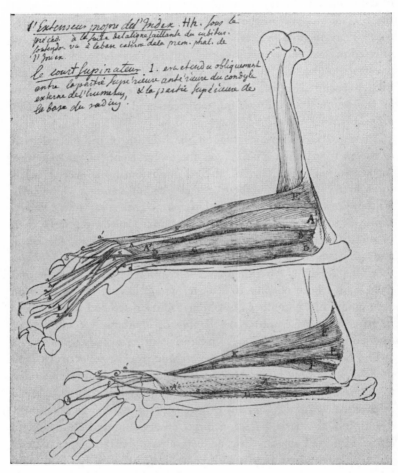

Dissection drawing by Cuvier of the medial and lateral musculature of the forelimb of the cat. The muscles are letter-keyed to the descriptions. Normandy, 1792. (MHN 608.)

mollusks, he considers this system in the crustacea (pp. 407–410). Whereas the heart of the decapods is oval, circumscribed, and centrally located in the thorax, that of the branchiopods is elongate, vaguely defined, and extends from one end of the animal to the other, almost as if it were nothing but a vessel itself. In the former group there are two principal vessels serving the branchiae, one arterial and the other venous, but in the branchiopods the venous blood returns to the heart via a pair of vessels in each segment through which the heart passes. The branchial arteries of the decapods arise from a thin, transparent ventral vessel; the origin of those in the other group was not yet clear, but Cuvier did not doubt that it was similar to that of the decapods. He then concluded that the circulation in these large groups is double, although only the aortic system possesses a heart (ventricle), and he added some comparisons with the circulatory apparatus of the gasteropod mollusks and the *vers à sang rouge*. The delicacy required in these dissections should be remarked. Presumably they were performed upon living specimens (the direction of the blood flow is observed) and the purposeful search which motivated them, the desire to discover the complete circulatory paths in these animals, is noteworthy. Two other points deserve notice. The study of the branchial circulation was completed by the use of anatomical injections, a colored fluid being forced through very fine vessels and its course observed. This was a long-familiar technique extensively employed by Cuvier. Secondly, he indicated what had been observed not to be present (auricles of the heart) and what had not been seen, even if perhaps present (the ventral vein in decapods and heart valves). A thorough investigator recognizes that even the negative aspects of his subject may be significant.

Cuvier strangely did not include in the *Leçons* his remarks on the general description of an animal. His own training and practice demonstrate that he regarded an authentic visual representation of the subject as the device least likely to mislead the student. A well-executed drawing possessed the advantage, as it still does, of per-

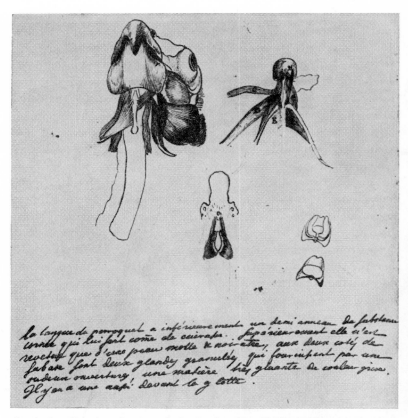

Perspective dissection drawing of the vocal organs of the parakeet. Cuvier here studies the organs as a functional unit and is not concerned with purely descriptive anatomy. This kind of anatomical procedure provided the factual basis for his functional anatomy. (MHN 614.)

mitting the anatomist to emphasize at will any particular structure; a muscle of the forearm could be portrayed in its entirety in an engraving whereas in the dissection itself it might be greatly obscured by adjacent structures. To avoid isolating the muscle, however, from its very real relations, several drawings would be necessary, some in plan, some in perspective. The plates for the *Leçons* are rather modest, almost schematic, illustrations. Those prepared by Cuvier himself are considerably more elaborate and complete. These drawings were first sketched in pencil and then reinforced with ink. Almost always the figures were keyed to verbal descriptions. Verbal description was of course the basis of the anatomical lectures and the published *Leçons*. Cuvier issued definite rules for description (IFFC 133, f. 50). The words employed, he said, must be clear and precise and conform to the existing rules of grammar, obvious requirements but ones often forgotten in the unstandardized anatomical language of the eighteenth century. Innovation was permitted with Latin words but almost never with the common tongue. The order of description was also important. Small details should never be permitted to obscure the major points under consideration. Description should begin with the general bearing of the animal and then descend by degrees to specific structural features. The style must be "simple and pure," eloquence and brilliance having no place in the scientific description of animals. The following brief example of Cuvier's scientific style, arid but clear and emphatic, is wholly typical of his writing.

Dans la *tortue*, les hémisphères forment un ovale. Leur partie antérieure est séparée de la postérieure par un sillon, et représente une espèce de bulbe qui sert comme de racine aux nerfs olfactifs. Ce bulbe est trois fois moindre que l'hémisphère. L'intérieur de l'hémisphère est creusé comme à l'ordinaire par un ventricule, et contient un corps analogue au cannelé, qui ressemble assez, pour la forme, à celui des oiseaux.

Les couches optiques ne sont pas plus grandes que les bulbes des nerfs olfactifs. Leur forme est à peu près arrondie: elles se prolongent en dessous et en avant sous les hémisphères pour produire le nerf optique. La valvule du cerveau se trouve entre elles et le cervelet, sans être sur-

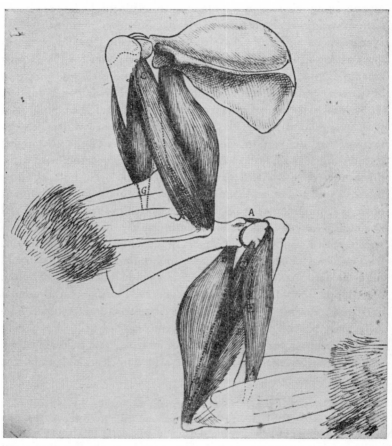

Dissection drawing of the muscles of the upper forelimb of the cat. Origins and insertions of the muscles are indicated. This is not a study in functional anatomy; Cuvier's aim was to describe these muscles in detail. Normandy, 1792. (MHN 608.)

montée ni précédée d'aucun tubercule, et elle donne, comme à l'ordinaire, naissance au nerf de la quatrième paire.[10]

Description, both visual and verbal, forms the substance of the *Leçons*. In the first volume, following over a hundred pages of introductory remarks, Cuvier treats the organs of movement, the skeletal and muscular systems. They are studied first as static, structural units in both the vertebrates and invertebrates and then their resultant actions are explained. Volume two is devoted exclusively to the nervous system, the organs of sensation. Brain, cranial nerves, the spinal cord and body nerves, and the special organs of the five senses are described. The first part of the study of the digestive system fills volume three, including descriptions of the jaws, teeth, throat, stomach, associated organs, and the vertebrate intestines. Volume four completes this description and adds that of the circulatory and respiratory systems and organs of voice. The final and shortest volume considers only the generative and excretory systems.

It should be noted that the principal concern of the articles in the *Leçons* is with the organs and organ systems of the body. Yet, by emphasizing the physiological dynamism of the organism and by drawing attention to its apparently molecular basis, Cuvier had committed himself to present at least a brief description of presumably more basic animal structures, that is, suborgan structures. The Introductions to the *Leçons* and to the *Règne animal* contain remarks on this question but a more complete presentation is found in the article "Animal" published in 1812.[11] A *tissu cellulaire*, Cuvier suggested, composed of innumerable small layers, cast about seemingly by chance, formed the membranes, canals, vessels, fibers, and hard parts of the body. The second basic structure was the *fibre irritable*, or muscle fiber, contractile and capable of convulsive movement; it formed the muscle bundles and covered many of the internal organs. Finally, there was the *substance médullaire*, neither contractile nor irritable but possessing the "wondrous" property of conducting sensations and the orders of the will. And that is all:

59

these three elements formed the solid framework of the organism and served as the regulators of the body fluids. The body was a mechanical system in continual change and the adult, nonpathological body as a persistent mechanical system in a changing environment was the primary fact of physiology. Theoretically, the facts of animal physiology were of great importance in Cuvier's zoological philosophy; practically, they appear to have meant almost nothing to him as an anatomist. In the latter occupation, Cuvier, like Aristotle and Vicq-d'Azyr before him, adopted the organs and the organ systems as the structural basis of the animal and the decision was perfectly consistent with the functionalist conception of vital organization, since, however much of the chemistry and intimate structure of living creatures had become known by 1800, the dominant theme among naturalists then in their maturity was still to consider digestion or respiration as typical organic functions. The day of a physiology relatively unprejudiced by gross structure lay yet in the future and Cuvier's system did little to encourage its rapid development.

Cuvier and comparative anatomy

The essential novelty of this immense work, the *Leçons*, did not belong to anatomical description but to anatomical comparison. Comparative anatomy received from Cuvier's hands a form so complete and a method so fruitful that one can accurately say that this science was, for all practical purposes, established between 1795 and 1805 and that the honor for this achievement belongs essentially to the *Leçons*. If one were seeking the true founder of comparative anatomy, a perhaps pointless occupation since rarely does a scientific discipline spring wholly from one mind, the obvious candidate would necessarily be Aristotle. Repeatedly in the *History of animals* he compared the structure of different animals, a procedure which naturally assumed at least some degree of similitude between the organs in question. Cuvier did not hesitate to give Aristotle premier position in the history of comparative anatomy, declaring that "the first author who compared the structure of animals and applied this knowledge to the elucidation of their natural history was Aristotle" (MHN 609, *prem. partie*). Galen's practice of using the Barbary ape as a model for human structure also suggested a basis for comparison, but individual anatomies and especially that of man, as noted above, long dominated anatomical investigation. Even Belon's famed illustration representing the skeleton of a bird beside that of a man was an isolated example. Not until the late seventeenth and early eighteenth centuries did comparison become, instead of an almost fortuitous accessory to anatomy, the primary aim of the science.[12]

Daubenton, it appears, was probably the major inventive spirit in France and his influence passed directly to Vicq-d'Azyr, who was, besides being a close friend and student, his son-in-law, and hence on to Cuvier. Daubenton's aim was only secondarily to effect comparisons; first must come description. In writing these descriptions for the *Histoire naturelle*, however, he deliberately followed the same order of presentation for every animal and this because, if "the descriptions must be compared [implying, obviously, that they must], there is no doubt that it is absolutely necessary to make them all on the same plan." [13] The actual comparison of the organs was left for the reader to perform, not at all a simple task since it would require either an incredible memory or the preparation of schematic charts for each group. Peter Camper (1722–1789), the great Leiden anatomist and osteologist, followed a more distinctly comparative method when establishing the facial angle of men of various races and different ages. This facial angle, the interior angle between a line running from the forehead to the chin and a second line from the base of the ear to the chin, was found by the comparison of a series of crania in Camper's large collection to be reasonably constant, and different, for each race of man. J. F. Blumenbach (1752–1840) at Göttingen compared as many characters of man as he was able, including cranial capacity, and not just the facial angle as Camper had done, and he too applied this knowledge to the races of man. Once again, however, the master was Vicq-d'Azyr. His physiological doctrine indicated how a first selection was to be made. Unfortunately he did not carry his selective analysis to conclusion, for, as Cuvier remarked in his brief notice, no less than 1339 individual anatomical features would have been required for the delimitation of each species in Vicq-d'Azyr's plan! The single published volume of his *Système anatomique des quadrupèdes* included descriptions of only the quadrumanes and the rodents. Principally to avoid repetition Vicq-d'Azyr had prepared summaries of the salient features of each family and, like those of Daubenton, each of these summaries followed a similar order of presentation. Other examples show more clearly his interest in relations and hence comparisons. A memoir of 1781 brought together anatomical data (on the brain) from several large animal groups. Not only did he compare the nervous structures of man, the quadrupeds, birds, fish, reptiles, and the insects-*vers*, but he established that mental ability is directly related to cerebral capacity and, further, since in the vertebrate forms at least the central nerve cord and the nerve network are similar, these mental differences must be sought in the structural differences of the higher parts (the cerebral hemispheres). This he did and concluded that, besides cranial capacity, the complexity of fissures and curvature of the cerebrum are equally valid anatomical indices of intelligence (p. 477). This is an already sophisticated comparative anatomy, lacking only in universal application to be almost indistinguishable from the science as we know it today.[14]

Cuvier's *Leçons* was the first truly complete work in the history of comparative anatomy. Whereas his predecessors, including Vicq-d'Azyr, had at best applied comparison to select groups of animals, he consistently attempted to employ it in his study of every known animal or species. Comparative anatomy became for Cuvier an essential segment of the theoretical basis of natural history. Just as chemistry uses attraction and geometry the angle, so, Cuvier declared, if the facts of natural history "can be reduced to a general theory, this would be philosophy par excellence . . . *Comparative*

62

anatomy is therefore the division of the natural sciences which tends to generalize, to erect the theory of organization." Comparative anatomy thus became the *regulatrice* of the other sciences: physiology is based on the organic functions ("no physiological theory is valid without comparative anatomy"); zoology arises from the structural bases of animals provided by comparative anatomy; even geology benefits from comparative anatomy, since the correlation of the parts is the assumed basis for the reconstruction of extinct animals from their fossil remains [IFFC 112(1), ff. 68–71].

Comparison was the principal key to the discovery of the secrets held by the empirical data of anatomy. It was a means of understanding experiments which only nature was able to perform. It was the source of the laws of anatomy. Writing in 1817, Cuvier said:

> The most fecund way of obtaining them [empirical laws] is comparison. It consists in successively observing the same body in its different natural positions, or in comparing different bodies among themselves as far as we know the constant relations between their structure and the phenomena which they manifest. These diverse bodies may be looked upon as a kind of experiment performed by nature, which adds or subtracts from each of these different parts (just as we try to do the same in our laboratories) and itself shows the results of these additions and subtractions.
>
> We are thus able to establish certain laws which rule these relations and are employed like those which are determined by the general [mathematical] sciences.[15]

All of the parts of the animal body being functionally interrelated, it seemed evident that experimental manipulation would destroy the living machine. Cuvier to a degree shared this fear with the physiologists previously mentioned (Chapter II), but he did not thereby condemn all experimentation. Lavoisier, Haller, and Galvani had shown that laboratory experimentation was more than satisfactory for the explanation of separate vital processes, but, as yet, no one had been able to devise any experimental techniques which could investigate the integral action of the organism. Cuvier believed that nature, fortunately, performed these experiments and that comparative anatomy, in tracing the various combinations of organs, at the same time revealed their physiological activity, since it was obvious that the organs were the determinants of any action whatsoever. The bond between physiology and anatomy had been sealed once again.

From his earliest anatomical works Cuvier had followed the comparative method whenever possible. Turning again to the *cahiers* prepared for the lectures on anatomy and later for the *Leçons* one finds, for example, a sketch of the comparisons to be made of the vertebrate muscles ("Ancien essai de myologie comparée," MHN 610). Heading several vertical columns placed on each folio are the names of various animals: *homme, singes, carnivores, rongeurs*, and so on. On the horizontal lines below each are inserted analogous muscles, the "same" muscles, when present or known, thus all appearing on the same line. Each folio is concerned with a separate set of muscles, divided by their cumulative action, for example, muscles moving the head on the trunk, the humerus on the trunk, the ribs on the spinal column; there are sixteen such categories. In each category Cuvier's catalogue is almost always most complete for man, and frequently there are few or no entries for certain of the other groups. Hence, the *cahier* is more useful in indicating gaps in knowledge than in providing a rapid synopsis of vertebrate musculature. Its importance, nevertheless, as a guide to Cuvier's method is in no way diminished by its incomplete state. A series of tables of this kind is an ideal comparative device which yields its conclusions the moment they are entered. Presence and absence, similarities of structure and function can all be read directly from the completed chart.

When translated into the *Leçons* the tabular form disappeared and was replaced by a strictly verbal presentation, the latter providing a greater opportunity to indicate exceptions, associated structures, functional peculiarities, and other data of anatomical importance. An example of comparison from the *Leçons* (III, 16–21) is the description of the internal angle of the lower jaw. This is a section of the general discussion of the jaw and the relations between the coronoid hypophyses and the condyle. It was first of all seen that this angle depended upon several factors: the prolongation of the muzzle, the length of the jaw bones, the number and size of the incisors and canines or the absence of teeth, and the nature of the junction of the bones at the chin. Beginning with man, the curvature and shape of the individual bones and their relations with tusks or beaks were considered in each of the vertebrate classes and with frequent references to particular species. Then only (pp. 29–102) were described the lower jaws of the vertebrates. From generalities on the jaw, meaning a comparison of this structure in the four vertebrate classes, Cuvier turned to the anatomical details upon which the former were based. The facts were important but, once established, became distinctly less interesting than the generalizations to which they had given birth.

The human body was not neglected by Cuvier and it often served as a model for his comparisons, but it must be recognized that human structure never preempted in Cuvier's anatomical studies the consideration of other vertebrates and invertebrates and that man was used primarily because of his greater familiarity. The *Tableau élémentaire* began with an extensive study of man but then turned, with his structure and behavior as the focal points, to the other animals. In the *Règne animal*, like the *Tableau* a taxonomic work, man became merely another animal, more perfect perhaps and decidedly more interesting to his own species, but nevertheless no model for the totality of other animals, even for the vertebrates. Each section of the *Leçons* always dealt first with human structure and a functional anatomy such as Cuvier's assumed as its basis a series of functions which were probably not fortuitously analogous to the range of vital processes of man. But, significant though this might be and no matter what taxonomic rank, even exclusive or dominating, one might wish to assign to the human species, there can be little doubt that, zoologically speaking, man no longer occupied his previous privileged position. Compare the place of man in Cuvier's anatomical studies and his place, for example, in the work of Vicq-d'Azyr and it is quickly seen how much anatomy had evolved under Cuvier's inspiration.

Inspiration is the most appropriate word here, for to praise Cuvier is neither to deny nor to denigrate the work of his numerous predecessors. Men such as P. S. Pallas, the Campers, Blumenbach, the Monros, and the Hunters were all able anatomists but, with the exception of Pallas, their principal interest lay always with man. Of Cuvier's early associates in Paris only Etienne Geoffroy Saint-Hilaire was an accomplished animal anatomist. The change in viewpoint from Vicq-d'Azyr to Cuvier perhaps may be explained by the fact that Vicq-d'Azyr was primarily a physician whereas Cuvier, although knowledgable in medical affiairs, had never followed medical studies and, of course, practiced medicine not at all. Between the physician and the naturalist there would be a great difference in interests and certainly this is true when one considers the breadth of Cuvier's zoological interests and the concentration by Vicq-d'-Azyr upon man and the vertebrates. For both, nevertheless, man was a physical and also a spiritual being and neither anatomist, Cuvier especially, would permit anatomy to encroach upon the rights of man's spiritual existence. With his soul, and also his mind, man did stand apart from the other animals, but this was not a sound reason, Cuvier believed, for the human body to be considered as the typical representative of either the vertebrates or the entire animal kingdom.

The *Leçons d'anatomie comparée* and his numerous other anatomical memoirs made of Cuvier the foremost anatomist of his day and raised anatomy itself to a level of comprehensiveness and perfection never before attained. The description of internal as well as external structure, the introduction of a greatly improved anatomical nomenclature aiming at the standardization of terms, and, above all, the consistent use of comparison all contributed to his achievement. All of this anatomical work was directed by Cuvier's intrinsic need for lawful forms of thought and pointed toward the

66

creation of a rational anatomy. Dissection and description could produce the clear and indisputable facts, and comparison could generalize them and reveal their real significance. The principal generalizations thus formed were the famous anatomical rules: the correlation of parts, which established the interrelated physiological operations and morphological features which guaranteed the life and integrity of the organism, and the subordination of characters, which determined the taxonomic value of the structures making up the organism.

The first anatomical rule

Actually, the two rules might be regarded as secondary corollaries of the unique fundamental postulate, the conditions of existence. Of the two rules, the correlation of parts is distinctly the more general and important. Daudin has suggested that there really was but one anatomical rule and that it be interpreted now toward the correlation, now toward the subordination of the parts or characters.[16] Cuvier himself insisted upon neither the name nor the separate existence of the two rules, and was content to trace their operation in concrete instances. The correlation of parts was a translation into anatomical terms of the conditions of existence.

Cuvier's principal theoretical discussion of the correlation of parts appeared in the section of the *Leçons* (I, 45–60) entitled *Tableau des rapports qui existent entre les variations des divers systèmes des organes*. Respiration, he declared, can act only through the intermediary of the movement of blood, since only in this manner can the blood reach the respiratory surfaces. Circulation in turn demands the support of the muscles, the heart being a muscular pump. Muscle contraction, finally, depends upon nervous stimulation. From these considerations he concluded that

it is in this mutual dependence of the functions and the aid which they reciprocally lend one another that are founded the laws which determine the relations of their organs and which possess a necessity equal to that of metaphysical or mathematical laws, since it is evident that the seemly harmony between organs which interact is a necessary condition of existence of the creature to which they belong and that if one of these functions were modified in a manner incompatible with the modifications of the others the creature could no longer continue to exist.[17]

In short, every organ of the body is functionally related to every other organ and from their cooperation arise the harmony and vigor of the organism. Cuvier stressed the fact that this was a physiological coordination and not a mere geometrical juxtaposition. It therefore happened that every abstract combination of organs, easily created by the imagination, did not necessarily exist and plainly often does not exist. The organs, in order to act "one upon another and concur toward a common goal," must be physiologically and not spatially determined. Thus, he continued, "those of these modifications which cannot exist together are reciprocally excluded, whereas the others are brought into existence." [18] Cuvier now possessed a physiological explanation for nonexistent animals and would later employ it as the basic argument for the necessary existence of gaps in the notorious zoological *série* (chain of being) and also in the sequence of fossil remains.

Not content with a mere general statement of the correlation of parts, he considered in detail the example of the relations between respiration, circulation, and movement and offered what he believed to be their functional explanation. Birds ("always in the air") were the most active vertebrate animals. Their muscles were powerful and could maintain their bodies suspended in air for long periods. The mammals were only slightly less active, holding themselves well above the ground, running rapidly, and climbing. The reptiles were a much more lethargic class of animals. Their locomotive organs were singularly inefficient and, when not slowly creeping along the surface of the earth, they were usually found hiding in caves or watery depths. The fish, however, never leaving their aqueous environment, were rapid swimmers and, supported by the water, could use their really moderate muscular force for efficient propulsion. Experiments having shown that "one of the principal actions of respiration is to restore to the [muscular] fiber its exhausted irritability," there had to exist an intimate connection between the degree of respiration and the mobility of the vertebrates. Thus the birds not only lived completely surrounded by the atmosphere but were, so to speak, surrounded within as well as without owing to the great air spaces and the hollow bones of their bodies. The mammals possesed a similar environment but were equipped only with lungs. Respiration seemed no more than an "accessory" affair for the reptiles, which often could suspend this function for long periods and whose whole life was passed "against the earth in obscure and stifled places in the middle of swampy mists." The fish occupied perhaps the most difficult habitat where the extraction of air from water was their foremost problem. Obviously the active birds had the greatest need for air and its oxygen; the conditions of existence therefore dictated that they should have the most efficient means for procuring it. The situation was similar for the mammals and the reptiles, the former possessing lungs with great absorbent surfaces and the latter employing relatively much-reduced respiratory organs. The absorbing capacity of each group was thus directly proportional to the needs generated by its muscular activity. This fortunate correlation is explained in the fish only by the related action of the circulation. Since the environmental fluid is water these creatures could obtain pure air only with difficulty and, the amount of air available to their body being proportional to the quantity of blood passing through their branchiae, the respiratory problem of the fish could be solved only by an accelerated pace of the circulation. This was the solution adopted by Cuvier: "the scant activity of the element [air dissolved in water] needs to be compensated for by the rapid return of the blood molecules in the pulmonary circulation." [19]

This discovery could not fail to lead to further generalizations and Cuvier was certainly provided with an adequate supply. Single and double circulation are thus explained. All animals respiring by means of branchiae and through the intermediary of water have a

69

double (and hence more efficient) circulation, a pulmonary and a systemic network of vessels. The fish correspond to this group. Among the air-breathing animals there occur both types of circulation. The birds and mammals are endowed with the double system; the reptiles (and amphibians) are frequently without a distinct pulmonary circulatory apparatus. The explanation of the situation in the latter classes is as obvious as it was above for the fish. The great activity of birds and mammals necessitates a rapid and effective restoration of the muscular force, requiring the appropriate circulatory systems, whereas the reptiles, lacking "excessive irritability," can be perfectly content with only a simple circulation.

At this point Cuvier was pleased to summarize his argument in a kind of arithmetical proportion of functional anatomy: a rapid death is proportional to rapid respiration, which is equivalent to a slow death being proportional to a slow rate of respiration. It seemed a fact that irritability, that is, muscular activity, was much less rapidly lost in dying animals as one descended the apparent vertebrate scale from mammals and birds to the reptiles and fishes. With the complete cessation of respiration, the birds and mammals quickly lost all muscular activity, but a similar cessation in the reptiles or fish was followed by more or less prolonged and increasingly uncoordinated movement. These facts, Cuvier believed, were explicable by the functional terms of the correlation of parts. The very efficient respiratory-circulatory systems of the birds and mammals, meaning both a plentiful supply of oxygen to the body and its almost immediate consumption in the tissues, yields a rapid reconstitution of the exhausted muscles and in these groups there will be little endurance after respiration is halted. The fish and reptiles, with a slower intake of oxygen and a reduced respiratory rate in the tissues, can continue to flop about after all external signs of respiration have stopped because their bodies will less rapidly consume their reservoir of oxygen. Respiration and irritability and also circulation were thus not only inseparably related but, Cuvier supposed, explained in physiologically meaningful terms.

The respiratory-circulatory process is a particularly complicated instance of the application of the first anatomical rule. Cuvier continued his discussion in the *Leçons* by next introducing the nervous system and then the digestive system into the web of functional interrelations. A much clearer and more concise presentation of the principle, now accepted as true doctrine and considered beyond the need of further exposition, appeared in the *Histoire naturelle des poissons*. Cuvier believed that at no moment could the correlation of parts speak more authoritatively than when deducing specific anatomical structures from a general, functional definition. Nothing could be more "clear and precise" than the modern "definition" of the fishes: "They are red-blooded vertebrate animals which respire by means of branchiae and the intermediary of water." [20] This was, he admitted, an empirical definition but it was also an observational formula whose correctness could be demonstrated by the deduction of the "entire nature" of the organism in question. First of all, he noted, in a classic example of circular argumentation, being vertebrates the fish must possess an internal skeleton, a brain and a nerve cord located within the spinal column, and the musculature situated externally to the skeletal system. They have only four appendages and their senses, save touch, are centered about the cranial cavity. Their aquatic environment means that they must be suited to a medium which, although supporting them, is more resistant than air. A muscular tail, short and flattened members, and smooth, hard scales instead of hair or feathers are the organs conveniently provided to overcome this resistance. Finally, the possession of branchiae means that the fish respire by means of water and that they will therefore be cold-blooded, have a lower vitality of muscles and sense organs, and have a much smaller brain than other vertebrates. Without air, they are mute; without illumination, the eyes are immobile; the ear detects only the loudest sounds (why hear in the "empire of silence"?); living only to swallow their prey, they have no need of taste; the sense of smell is useless to them and the tactile sensations are obscured or lost by the hard scales and inflexible limbs. Why does this almost insensate bag of organs, an animal whose *amours* are "cold like themselves," which knows none of the pleasures of nesting or mating, exist? It exists, Cuvier replied, only to lead a life of bland reproduction, searching for prey and being itself pursued, nothing more. Even the brilliant patterns and colors with which the fish are decorated mean nothing to these animals themselves. They seemed to exist only to satisfy man's aesthetic pleasures and to call his attention to an exceptionally fertile source of food. Here certainly was the correlation of parts stated as nakedly as it was conceived. The subtilties have vanished; the dogma remained.

Not only were the organs proportional to the functions which they subserved but, from another point of view, the functions had to be directly proportioned to the degree of organ complexity. "It is one of the conditions of existence of any animal," said Cuvier, "that its needs must be proportional to the faculties which it has to satisfy them." [21] Perhaps the most striking example of this relation concerns the interaction of the nervous system and the muscle actions. Birds and mammals, with a relatively highly developed central nervous system, can experience "vigorous sensations and strong passions," while the lowly fish and reptiles, with much reduced cranial capacity, are subject to greatly diminished stimulation. These circumstances, Cuvier believed, unquestionably arose from the modest muscular force of the fish and reptiles because, should these two groups be exposed to excessive nervous activity, that is, should their nervous systems be more like those of the birds and mammals, they would be subjected to passions which would immediately overwhelm their relatively slight muscular resources. Naturally the birds and mammals, possessing a more effective musculature, can endure and utilize the commands of their equally refined nervous systems.

Conclusion

Here was an articulate and accomplished rational anatomy. The structure and behavior of the fishes had been "reasoned" from their definition, and their definition was believed to be empirical, analytic, and exhaustive. It is interesting to observe the significant difference between Cuvier's view of rational anatomy and that made famous under the same name by his colleague, Etienne Geoffroy Saint-Hilaire. Like Cuvier, Geoffroy had understood rational anatomy to mean the deliberate quest for the general rules of the science. Unlike Cuvier, however, he laid down rules that were idealistic in form and substance and the greatest effort of his lifetime was to establish the structural unity apparently present among all animals. Geoffroy imposed a highly speculative, Platonic conception of animal form upon data which he, as one of the most skillful and experienced anatomists of his day, had helped to discover.[22] Cuvier's correlation principle was certainly not an empirical law. But, unlike the unity principle upon which Geoffroy erected his science, it did not stand directly in contradiction to known facts. To Cuvier, lack of contradiction too often was considered to mean confirmation. Thus, when applying the term "rational" to Cuvier's conceptions, no more is meant than the identification of his professed empirical determination of accepted laws of nature. If these Cuvierian laws were really not empirical, neither were they as divorced from the elementary facts of anatomy as were the highly imaginative creations of Geoffroy.

The principle of the correlation of parts, however unreasonable or lacking in empirical justification it may actually have been, was the very heart of Cuvier's reformed and rational anatomy. When observed from without, it is seen to be not an empirical rule at all but a direct consequence of the Aristotelian picture of the biological world. It was of course precisely the kind of law which Cuvier had been seeking. It was self-evident, general, and fecund. It was, above all, a law, a rule, a principle, and this was itself the aim (or the commencement) of the Cuvierian anatomical endeavor. Cuvier had formed the vision of lawfulness in anatomical science, even if he perhaps failed in its realization.[23]

IV

A New Classification of Animals

*The history of animals no longer displays
the arbitrary and irregular progress that
it had twenty years ago; it has become a
rational science.* — CUVIER [1]

THE principle of the subordination of characters was Cuvier's second anatomical rule. It meant no more than the establishment of the relative value of the various parts of the organism. It was proposed and developed in answer to the long-standing problem of ascertaining these values for the innumerable characters used to classify the animals. Cuvier, like Vicq-d'Azyr, was perplexed by the uncertain manner in which morphological features were employed as taxonomic guides. Not until 1812, with the determination of four broad zoological categories based upon the nervous system, was he satisfied that animal systematics had finally found its true and precise form.

Combining the principle of the subordination of characters with that of the correlation of parts, Cuvier arrived at his best-known classificatory generalization, the *type* concept. Every taxonomic category, from species and genus to the *embranchement*, was, he believed, a sharply defined and morphologically stable unit. The zoological *type*, at all levels, became Cuvier's practical unit of classification, although it continued to carry the names of the current taxonomic divisions. A highly rationalized hierarchy of organic functions, in addition to firm insistence upon the unchangeable and irreducible taxonomic elements (*types*), were thus the central features of Cuvier's prolonged efforts to classify the animal kingdom.

The subordination of characters naturally assumed that each animal part possessed a distinct value, which it was both possible and desirable for the naturalist to discover and employ. A knowledge of the conditions of existence or their anatomical expression, the correlation of parts, would in itself have been of little use in the classification of animals. The correlation of parts spoke of the overall functional condition of each individual animal and dictated the structural interrelations which were necessary for this creature to maintain its healthful integrity and existence. In its primitive form, the first anatomical rule offered no means of distinguishing one organism from another, except that it implied a crude knowledge of the complete organization of any given animal. No salient features were suggested, no basic functions were exalted by this rule, and practical classification required a far greater refinement of identifying characteristics than could be obtained from an exhaustive but undigested *précis* of each animal.

A need for abridgement was more evident to Cuvier than it had previously been to Vicq-d'Azyr. In the first place, the number of animal specimens and species available for study had again increased enormously (see Chapter I). Exploration, almost halted during the Revolutionary and Napoleonic wars, had recommenced thereafter with great animation and, although only a small part of this material was available for the original edition of the *Règne animal*, the steadily increasing bulk of later editions testifies to the magnitude of the new collections. Furthermore, these wars were not wholly detrimental to the French collections since the French troops, particularly under Napoleon, performed numerous depredations on European museum collections, in zoology as well as in the arts, and carried back their prizes to Paris and the Muséum. Cuvier would later be pleased to recall his own great service to the Muséum when, during the negotiations for the return of the captured treasures which followed the Hundred Days, he was instrumental in keeping in Paris the large and magnificent collection of the Stadholder of Holland.[2] To all of this material must be added that which was contributed by the regular activity of the Muséum naturalists, an activity which, if Cuvier himself may serve as an index, continued unabated from 1795 until the fiasco of 1812 and which again bloomed under the *Restauration*. Indeed, natural history collections appeared to augment even more rapidly after the Revolution than they had during the eighteenth century.

In speaking of his *Règne animal*, Cuvier confessed that he possessed enough material for numerous volumes and that the problem was to invent some "abridged means of presentation." His solution, if not ingeniously original, was so logical and so successfully applied that it has scarcely been modified during the past century and a half. He attributed his success to the use of *"généralités graduées,"* to never repeating for a species what had been said for its subgenus, and for a genus what was noted for its order, and so on. In this manner one attained the "greatest economy of words," the beauty and "principal aim" of his work.[3] The organization of the *Règne animal* closely followed this plan, the major groups being discussed first (for example, birds), then the order (birds of prey), the genus, and the species (common vulture). The characterization of each group became more specific as one descended the hierarchy of taxa. The description of each higher group always included all those groups placed directly below it. Conversely, as one mounted from the species to the class each description became less individual and more general and the common features of an increasing number of organisms became apparent.

The formal arrangement of a book was only one means of classifying the animal kingdom. It was a mechanical device rather than a rational procedure. It said nothing of the essence of the animals which were dropped into its convenient categories because, being only a naked taxonomic skeleton, it was not based upon these ani-

76

mals at all. This kind of formal arrangement, which concisely represents for us today what we hope is an approximate scheme of the phylogenetic history of the animal kingdom, was for Cuvier an economical means of presenting the animals. It was an arrangement which was based not upon what he believed were the spurious tales of historical zoology but upon the principle of the subordination of characters, the second anatomical rule.

The subordination of characters

In its definitive form the Cuvierian taxonomic system was based upon the four *embranchements*, each of which was in turn defined by a complex of *caractères importants*. Below the most important characters descended the secondary and tertiary features which increasingly divided the animal kingdom. This, in theory, was the principle of the subordination of characters. Cuvier stated the idea most clearly in the *Règne animal*:

> For a good classification . . . we employ an assiduous comparison of creatures directed by the principle of the *subordination of characters*, which itself derives from the conditions of existence. The parts of an animal possessing a mutual fitness, there are some traits of them which exclude others and there are some which require others; when we know such and such traits of an animal we may calculate those which are coexistent with them and those which are incompatible; the parts, properties, or consistent traits which have the greatest number of these incompatible or coexistent relations with other animals, in other words, which exercise the most marked influence on the creature, we call *caractères importants, caractères dominateurs*; the others are the *caractères subordonés*, and there are thus different degrees of them.[4]

Because all combinations of parts are not possible or equally common, various organisms are, in their grand traits, clearly distinct. This has been shown to be a consequence of the conditions of existence and the first anatomical rule. The obvious problem for any systematic use of a hierarchy of characters becomes the precise determination of which characters are more important and which are of lesser importance. Cuvier, it appears, adopted in theory one answer to this question but was compelled in practical taxonomic work to employ also its alternative.

The latter alternative, the morphological constancy of characters (in place of their deduced functional importance), had recently been stated in a convincing and influential form by Antoine Laurent de Jussieu. His treatise, the *Genera plantarum*, is one of the great landmarks in the history of taxonomic botany.[5] This work, a recapitulation and development of numerous memoirs published by the Académie des sciences since 1773, sought to define as clearly as possible the higher botanical taxonomic categories by employing characters of unquestionable certainty. De Jussieu's first division of the plant kingdom established three categories which are still today primary botanical divisions (acotyledons, monocotyledons, and dicotyledons). They were founded upon the number of seed leaves (cotyledons). Each of these three primary groups was then distributed, using the number of petals or the position of the ovary and stamens, or both, into a total of 15 classes, the most important practical taxonomic units.

Cuvier was much impressed by de Jussieu's volume. He wrote to Pfaff (November 1790) that he could not "admire too greatly the intelligence with which the plants are distributed" and their features analyzed and stated. Twenty years later, referring to de Jussieu's use of the important characters as the basis for a natural classification of plants, Cuvier favorably compared his innovation in botany to the revolution effected in chemistry by Lavoisier and his collaborators. What Cuvier seemed to admire most — and his approval may be judged by the degree to which he employed these ideas — was the possibility of being able to build one's classification upon them. De Jussieu had himself remarked that the "difference in value of the characters has introduced into contemporary botany, if not a positive geometry, at least a kind of computation [*calcul*] which becomes perfected in measure as the relative values are better determined." Any botanist, he had argued, soon began to recognize that various plants were delimited by certain sets of common characters. Further observation disclosed that among these characters there were some which were "plus constans, plus importans" than the others. From this it was concluded that those characters which were most constant were precisely those which were most important. It must be realized that these characters were important in a taxonomic sense, that is, being constant they quite literally were important for a stable and consistent system of division. Their taxonomic value revealed nothing necessarily of their role in the plant economy, and they were therefore almost wholly indifferent to functional importance. De Jussieu's real innovation was to use these characters as the basis for a rigorous system of calculation of taxonomic rank. The use of constant characters was itself a long-established and acceptable practice in botany.[6]

Ostensibly, this was not the case for Cuvier. His entire theoretical framework required that importance be determined by functional criteria. This was demanded by his interpretation of the conditions of existence and certainly the subordination of characters can have no other meaning. To discover the reason for this opposition of belief between Cuvier and de Jussieu is not a simple task. Perhaps one answer might be found in the material itself. The plants are immobile and without obvious organ activity, whereas the animals are mobile and sensitive, and many of them give immediate signs of the activity which their organs possess. Every aspect of an animal seems to be dynamic and thus demands a functional attitude. Furthermore, the Aristotelian prejudice that growth and reproduction were the essential activities of the plant while the animal possessed in addition sensibility and movement reinforces the functional viewpoint of a zoologist. The most likely explanation, however, seems to emerge from Cuvier's own primary objectives. It is difficult not to believe that he found the functional approach more satisfying because he felt that it was more "philosophical." The botanical method was certainly valuable and valid; the induction of the important features of a plant group was just that much more indisputable knowledge gained. Cuvier liked to believe that he himself had carried his science (zoology) beyond sophisticated empiricism (botany). He had advanced one step, perhaps the definitive step, beyond de Jussieu and the botanists and had raised zoology, thanks to his two anatomical rules and all that they implied, to the level of a rational science. Besides, what rational value could one assign to stamen insertion, petal number, or a divided calyx; would these values appear as reasonable as those given to the brain, the heart, or the teeth? The botanists' concentration upon the reproductive organs was in part due to the influence of the Aristotelian idea of reproduction as an essential plant function. De Jussieu, no less than Cesalpino and Linnaeus before him, had recognized this but it appears to have remained only a secondary consideration for him. The following *dictum*, given as the basic rule of taxonomy, shows how important constancy was in his mind.

The characters, in computation [*calcul*], must not be counted as unities but each according to its relative value, so that a single constant character may be equivalent or even superior to several inconstant, united characters.[7]

Cuvier's statements on this question are, at best, ambiguous. In the *Tableau élémentaire* (note, p. 4) he remarked that the "more constant relations" are those which belong to the "most important parts," and that it is these parts which exercise the greatest influence on the organism. The memoir of 1812 establishing the four *embranchements* declared that the maximum utility of a classification depended upon its reduction to least terms, that is, to its most general propositions. The subordination of characters, which "consists in giving to the most general groups characters drawn from the most influential organs, or the most constant," would lead to the desired end.[8] Finally, in the *Règne animal* (I, 11–12) Cuvier admitted that the "influence of the characters is sometimes determined in a rational manner by the consideration of the nature of the organ" but that in other cases one must use "simple observation" since a "sure means" of recognizing the important characters is to dis-cover those which are most constant. Importance and constancy stemmed from the "very nature itself" of the organs.

Why, for example, in the memoir of 1812 is the nervous system considered the most important complex of characters? Were the brain, nerves, and sense organs the most unvarying organs of the animal body, or were these parts functionally the most important elements of an organism? There is no question as to which of these alternatives Cuvier preferred. Rational science, founded upon the empirical data, was his ideal. He complained that in botany, since the plants for the most part had neither sensory nor motive organs and the naturalist was forced to employ their reproductive parts as the fundamental characters, "once we depart from the composition of the seed we have scarcely any a priori reasons to give for con-stancy." [9] It is clear that an a priori, functional explanation of im-portance was the primary goal of the systematist. It is also clear that such explanations were unfortunately not always available (if they existed at all). The passage from the *Règne animal* (I, 10) dis-closes the flexibility of Cuvier's thought on this subject. His argu-ment, if not actually a circular one, declares that both viewpoints are correct. It further suggests that, although functional influence must be accorded the primary position, in its absence physical con-stancy is sufficient. Physical constancy would have added meaning for an experienced anatomist. He would know that there are cer-tain organs or organ systems which were, so to speak, constant; for example, the shape and action of the heart of the dog is more con-stant from individual to individual than the color of the beast's hair or the pattern of the minute ramifications of the capillary sys-tem. He would also know that various taxonomic groups were on the whole composed of organisms possessing characteristic features which were distinct from those of other groups. This was known by experience. It was the basis of innumerable taxonomic divisions, particularly of that division called the species, a unit frequently al-most intuitively formed by the field naturalist.

One might reasonably conclude, therefore, that Cuvier's principle of the subordination of characters is quite literally a rationalization of the empirical evidence. The importance and application of this principle must not for this reason be discounted. With regard to the species the principle was almost completely inapplicable but it enjoyed a greater success with higher taxonomic units, the families and classes, and it was these elevated groups which received Cuvier's special attention. He had mastered perhaps as completely as any of his contemporaries the seemingly limitless catalogue of species and genera and he now required a device by which these modest units could be meaningfully incorporated within a general classification of all organic nature. For this purpose surely the subordination of characters was a singularly happy discovery. Not only did it seem to receive frequent confirmation from below, that is, its declarations were supported by the physical constancy of the relevant parts, but it enjoyed the generality and reasonableness which belonged to it as a corollary of the first anatomical rule.

The means of determination within this system of the relative importance of the anatomical parts (characters) thus cannot be categorically established. Physical constancy seemed to be the basis of any particular taxonomic unit, but the deduced functional importance of the parts gave the completed classificatory apparatus its form and its intelligibility. Cuvier did not disguise his frequent appeal to constancy, but neither did he hesitate to attempt to place it in its proper position: absolutely inferior to the principle of the subordination of characters and its functional interpretation.

Cuvier's early attempts at classification

Attention has been called above to the absence of any permanent order of functional and structural importance in the anatomical doctrines of Vicq-d'Azyr and to his proposal of several different lists of organs. Cuvier's subordination of characters in its earlier forms was also troubled by an uncertainty of the correct order. Not until 1812 would Cuvier finally publish his definitive views on the subject, although these ideas had been with him certainly since 1807 and possibly since 1803.

The first exposition of the subordination of characters appeared in two important memoirs published in 1795. The first of these memoirs, prepared in collaboration with Etienne Geoffroy Saint-Hilaire, suggested a new classification of the mammals. It was hoped that the division of this class would proceed on wholly rational grounds. The first step was to establish specific values for the relevant characters. Since some organs constituted the very *existence* of an animal and others placed the creature in *rélation* with its neighbors and the world, in the author's words "car l'animal est d'abord, et puis il sent et agit," the essential functions must be reproduction, movement, and circulation, the latter serving to maintain the organism.[10] Reproduction provided the characters of the class of mammals itself: viviparous birth and the suckling of the young by mammae. For the internal divisions of the class one must turn to the organs of relation. Nutrition, being more or less peculiar to each species, gives excellent taxonomic characters and thus a combination of the number and the kinds of teeth (crushing, tearing, biting; molar, canine, incisor) provided useful characters. The most basic of the senses, the key function of *rélation*, is touch, and this is dependent upon the digits and their covering. Curiously, the manner of movement was not considered a sound classificatory tool. The organs of movement were thought to be much too varied to permit any coherent system to be based upon them, an argument which even further betrays Cuvier's views on constancy and importance. From among these characters are selected the most important indices for classification, the first being the nature of the coverings of the digits (sensation), then the number and form of the teeth (nutrition), and, finally, the nature of the limbs (movement).

Only the first subdivision of the mammals was created by these rules. Three divisions, called *embranchements* but not to be confused with the categories later (1812) denoted by this term, were formed: (*a*) marine mammals ("doights réunis en nageoires"), (*b*) hoofed mammals ("doights envelopés du corne"), and (*c*) mammals with nails. But (*a*) is then subdivided into three *familles* by the number of limbs, while (*b*) is divided into three *familles* by the number of digits. The mammals with nails are subdivided into nine *ordres* by the number of teeth and by the organs of touch (digits).[11]

This was a clever system of classification which quickly forgot theoretical propositions and employed those characters whose nature or prominence commanded attention. Below the *embranchements* no consistent application was made of the various degrees of importance. In one case the limbs were used, in another the digits, and in still another the teeth. The orders, families, and genera were all based upon characters wholly relative to the materials at hand. Unifying anatomical criteria were not applied at equivalent stages of the process.

A procedure very similar to that followed with mammals was employed in the second memoir of 1795 in the classification of the so-called *vers*. This class had long served as an example of the inadequacies of the Linnaean zoological system. Given the same taxonomic rank as the relatively homogeneous classes of mammals, birds, reptiles, fish, and "insects," the *vers* included an incredibly wide range of quite dissimilar organisms. One found here mollusks, echinoderms, terrestrial and marine worms, polyps, the vast and amorphous group of the zoophytes, and other small creatures. Whatever advantage was gained by a reasonably precise definition of certain of these species was lost in the complete incoherence of their overall relationships. The class of *vers* was characterized more by its negative features (nonvertebrated, non-red-blooded) than by any possible invention of common characters, and this was merely a consequence of the essential heterogeneity of the species which the class had attempted to embrace.

"In the other classes," Cuvier remarked, "I find many exceptions; here [*vers*] everything is an exception." [12] After pondering the dif-

84

ferences which so divided the *vers*, he believed he had discovered the key to their resolution and this key was, of course, the subordination of characters. The same principle could thus be applied throughout the entire animal kingdom. Although the principle seemed therefore universal, the results of its calculation were not. Cuvier recalled from his mammalian study the importance of the production and maintenance of life and hence of generation and circulation. Once again generation is such a generalized process among the *vers*, a group for the most part either oviparous or gemmiparous, that it provided no convenient and distinctive marks for the systematist. Circulation was the next most basic function of these animals and its apparatus presented ample classificatory characters. Cuvier deduced (rather, categorically stated) three divisions from the circulatory apparatus: animals with a heart, complete vascular system, and respiratory branchiae; animals with only a muscular dorsal vessel and tracheae; and animals with neither heart nor vessels and without special respiratory organs. In order to create subdivisions of these groups, Cuvier turned to the immediately inferior characters, those of the nervous system, and in the class of the *vers* this meant the presence or absence, or modifications, of the brain and the "medulla" (the term for any sizable nerve mass, often anterior, but apparently lacking the complexity of a brain).

The ensuing division of the Linnaean *vers* resulted from a combination of these two character complexes, the nervous and the circulatory organs, and it refounded completely what we call today invertebrate taxonomy. Cuvier's classification was quickly adopted by Lamarck and was then expanded and modified. Cuvier himself later suggested several changes in his own classification. In this early classification, the single class (*vers*) was divided into six new classes, all of equal rank: *mollusques, crustaces, insects, vers, echinodermes*, and *zoophytes*. The *mollusques* were naturally the most complex creatures, with heart, vessels, and brain. Most simple were the zoophytes, almost nothing more than "aggregations of tubes and globules in constant motion." The new class of *vers*, with a segmented body, nerve cord, and a simple dorsal vessel, has since been further subdivided; in Cuvier's system it included almost all of the animals popularly known as worms.

Cuvier in this memoir did not bother to describe species, or even genera. He followed very closely the prime intention of all of his taxonomic work: description and explanation and not mere identification. This is explicitly stated in the memoir on the *vers*:

> In conclusion, I have not presented this essay on division that it may serve as the beginnings of the determination of the names of species; an artificial system would be easiest for this, and this is only proper. My aim has been to make known more exactly the nature and true relationships of the *animaux à sang blanc* [a collective term for the modern subkingdom of the invertebrates], by reducing to general principles what is known of their structure and general properties.[13]

Here, more clearly than elsewhere, for example, in the enormous bulk of the *Règne animal*, are seen the motivation and direction of Cuvier's thought and practice in animal classification.

The organs of circulation, supplemented by those of nutrition and respiration, served as the bases for the taxonomic procedure in Cuvier's next two major works. The system in the *Tableau élémentaire* was deliberately simplified, the volume being written as a primer of zoology. The first division separated the animal kingdom into *animaux à sang rouge* and *animaux à sang blanc*.[14] The former were then divided into warm- and cold-blooded animals and, by mode of reproduction and respiration, into the usual vertebrate classes. The *animaux à sang blanc* retained the divisions from the memoir on the *vers*. In the *Leçons d'anatomie comparée* no lengthy discussion of these problems is attempted, but Cuvier did append to the first volume of the set several large folding tables, on which he schematically represented his conception of the correct classification of animals. Once again the bases for classification are circulation and nutrition. Each of the tables deals with one of the nine classes established by Cuvier. For the first and also, as a term for a distinct taxonomic unit, for the last time he uses the words *vertébrés* and *invertébrés*, proposed by Lamarck in 1797 and almost universally accepted by naturalists.[15] The terms were later used by Cuvier as convenient labels for two large groups of animals, but they naturally lost all rigorous systematic meaning for him when he established the four *embranchements*. The subsequent division of these groups is again based upon the color and temperature of the blood, and the presence or absence of circulatory vessels, respiratory system, reproductive mechanisms, and other parts.

In all of this taxonomic work, published between 1795 and 1800, there is no positive, definite espousal of a unique, fundamental physiological index for the entire animal kingdom. Sometimes the circulatory system, other times the nutritive organs or those of locomotion or sensation, are employed. Cuvier at this point has, by his own standards, advanced beyond Vicq-d'Azyr only in recognizing the need for a stabilized hierarchy of functions; his search for this order had been so far unsuccessful. Once, however, he had rediscovered the critical role of the nervous system in the animal economy success came rapidly and the system of the four *embranchements* was born.

The four embranchements

In 1803 there appeared in yet another of the grand encyclopedias of natural history so popular in the early nineteenth century an article by J. J. Virey, erudite and pharmacist.[16] Virey's article was intended to be a general introduction to the subject of zoology. The distinction between animals and plants, the role of the animal in the economy of nature, and the structure and functions of the animal were studied and discussed. To this article, it appears, belongs the honor of having suggested to Cuvier the basis for the creation of the four *embranchements*.

Virey argued that the primary characteristic of an animal was *sensibilité*. This was nothing but the old Aristotelian opinion and one which has already been seen favorably received by Cuvier. Virey continued his analysis and established, after Buffon, the similitude of animals and plants based on their *mobilité*. The reference to plants seems to have been added merely to complete the discussion; whether plants are or are not mobile was quite incidental to his object. The third characteristic was nutrition, internal among the animals, external among the plants. From these distinctions Virey was able to present a definition of the animal (pp. 425–426): "a sensitive, organized body, moving at will, which possesses a central organ of digestion."

Since, as Virey quaintly remarked, all animals do not enjoy the "same dose of animality," the naturalist (whose aim was to classify as well as to probe the essence of animals) needed some device to measure the various degrees of animality. The definition itself of an animal suggested this instrument. By determining the relative preponderance of each of the three prime organ systems — sensation, mobility, and nutrition — in each of the animals, the naturalist should be able to form estimates of their appropriate position in the taxonomic system. Of the three, the nervous system must predominate. Virey's final division, a rather simple and inelegant affair, produced three essential *tribus* or *divisions* (p. 432): animals with both a cerebral and a sympathetic nervous system (man, mammals, birds, reptiles, and fish); animals with one nervous system only and that surrounding the esophagus (mollusks, crustacea, insects, *vers*); and animals with mere nervous "molecules" (zoophytes, echinoderms, sponges, and corals). Unfortunately for the consistency of the scheme, the subdivisions separating, for example, the birds and the fish, or the crustacea and the *vers*, bear no relation to Virey's theoretical postulates. Instead of the organs of motion and nutrition, the traditionally convenient characters of blood temperature, absence or presence of a heart, and so on are employed. Like Cuvier, he found the categories vertebrate and invertebrate useful but not sufficiently related to systems of real functional importance. The familiar distinction between the *animaux à sang rouge* and *animaux à sang blanc* had been already vitiated by Cuvier's discovery of a sizable group of (annelid) worms possessing veritable

88

red blood.[17] Cuvier had rejected this plan in the *tableaux* published in the *Leçons* and Virey contributed nothing new to the problem.

The importance of Virey's article lies in its deliberate use of the organs of the nervous system as the primary characters for zoological classification. Cuvier quietly acknowledged his debt to Virey in a brief reference, in the Preface to the *Règne animal*, to the latter's article of 1803. He was more explicit when preparing a review, in the lecture series on the history of science, of his own memoir of 1812 which first publicly presented the four *embranchements*. He remarked (IFFC 94, f. 169): "The nonvertebrated animals differ more among themselves than do the vertebrated. They must therefore not be considered in some way as the second half of the kingdom. Four general forms determined by the nervous system. See Virey, *nouv. dict. art. animal.*"

From the very fact of their overwhelming importance and general distribution, the organs of the nervous and locomotory systems had at first appeared to Cuvier as unacceptable taxonomic guides. An undated but obviously early (before 1807) manuscript discussing the problems of zoological classification suggests that Cuvier was compelled or desired to retain the familiar characters drawn from the blood, respiratory activity, and mode of reproduction and to disregard the organs of movement or sensation (IFFC 172, ff. 4–9). The latter organs were so important to the animal economy and hence so unvarying, relative to the organs of the secondary functions, that he believed their systematic value was greatly reduced. What Virey had shown was that the nervous system, always suspected of being the most important system although often given only verbal recognition, could provide tangible characters for classification. The nervous system was not everywhere the same but varied according to the degree of "animality" of the animals. To possess a practical taxonomic tool which simultaneously represented the most important of all animal functions satisfied as no other system could Cuvier's desire for a precise classification based upon a rational anatomy.

It was only after reading Virey's article, that is, after 1803, that Cuvier formulated in his mind the distribution of the animal kingdom into four *embranchements*. Although a full statement of the idea was not to appear for another seven years, the idea itself had definitely been formed by 1807, if not actually earlier. He began in 1807 a sequence of three extremely important series of lectures, the second being delivered in 1809 and the course concluded by a final series in 1812. The course professedly concerned itself with comparative anatomy, but was really directed toward the application of anatomical discoveries to animal classification. The three series, composed of some one hundred lectures, were never published, but the notebooks (IFFC 104, 105) upon which they were based were preserved by Cuvier and undoubtedly were at his side when he composed the memoir of 1812 and the *Règne animal*. These notebooks give evidence of considerable preparation for the statement of generalities but of much less attention to the sections concerned with anatomical detail.

From the outset one is struck by the contrast between these lectures and those which, begun a dozen years earlier, ultimately formed the five volumes of the *Leçons*. In the *cours* of 1807–1812 Cuvier adopted a new plan of presentation; his aim was now different. Instead of a preliminary discussion of the organic functions and their organs and of the animals, to be followed by a general and all-inclusive review of each function and its associated parts, he was now in possession of the most important system, the nervous system, and undertook to develop fully the taxonomic consequences which he suspected were hidden in the nerves and muscles of animals. No longer was there a need for exhaustive reviews of each organ system; rather, one must concentrate on the basic functions. Thus the series of 1807 was devoted exclusively to the nervous system and that for 1809 considered only the locomotive organs. In 1812 Cuvier attempted to generalize his findings and to add what remarks were necessary on the other vital activities. In 1807 the brain, central nervous system, and sense organs were described in great detail. The next most important system, that which carried out the orders of the nervous system, was that giving mobility to the animal and in 1809 Cuvier described and catalogued, frequently incompletely and with obvious haste, the skeletal members, muscles, tendons, and associated nerves for the majority of the relevant animal groups.

Functionalism was still the foundation of the system, but it had now at last discovered its true principles. Cuvier would never again be uncertain about which was the most "important" function. The relation of the nervous system to the organs of motion was, he believed, equally clear and each of the other functions would in turn find its proper place by being judged in relation to the two preceding functions. He declared in 1807 that "the nervous system is the essence of the animal. It is by its means that [the animal] exists, that it has an individuality . . . The other organs are destined to maintain it or to satisfy its needs: digestion, circulation, respiration, locomotory system. Nevertheless, in its turn, it maintains and animates them." The importance of the nervous system was first announced in the second lecture of the same series. The motive organs were particularly valuable, he added, when opening the next series, because, once their "principle" is admitted, they lend themselves admirably to a very exact determination of characters, where the forms of bones and articulations, the direction, size, and strength of muscles, and the muscle-bone interactions can all be established with almost mathematical certainty. No better characters could be desired, although of course they would have meaning only for the vertebrates.[18]

If the reevaluation of the role of the nervous system provided a new technique for the general classification of the animal kingdom, it alone was not the inspiration for the recasting of the zoological classes. Cuvier had long been dissatisfied with his classifications of 1795, 1798, and 1800. The class of the vertebrates posed no general problems; it was easily recognized as a distinct group based on positive characters. The great mass of invertebrate divisions remained, however, uncertain. Were the crustacea as general a group, as "elevated" a category, as, for example, the insects? Were the zoo-phytes a distinct group or were they merely a receptacle for small, often poorly known animals, perhaps totally unrelated to one another? The changing face of his previous classifications renders obvious Cuvier's uncertainty before these questions. A wholly new tone, one speaking with authority, entered in 1812, and this because Cuvier believed that he had discovered the source of his errors. To the question of what was wrong with his earlier systems, Cuvier replied that, "too respectful of previous usages," he had given "the title of class to groups of very different rank." His class of mollusks, he recognized, by the "importance of its general characters and the variety of creatures of which it is composed, [is] equivalent to the entire series of the vertebrates." Either the mollusks must form several new classes, or all of the vertebrates must be united into a single new class.[19]

Cuvier preferred to unite the four vertebrate "classes" into one Class of the Vertebrates and he placed at an equal level the Mollusks, the Articulata, and the Radiata. These were the famous four *embranchements* which would form the basis of all of his subsequent taxonomic work. He announced his creation in unequivocal words:

> In considering the animal kingdom from this point of view and being concerned with only the animals themselves, and not with their size, usefulness, our knowledge of them, great or small, or any other accessory circumstances, I have found that there exist four principal forms, four general plans, upon which all of the animals seem to have been modeled and whose lesser division, no matter what names naturalists have dignified them with, are only modifications superficially founded on development or on the addition of certain parts, but which in no way change the essence of the plan.[20]

He added that it had been his experience during the past several years which compelled him to advance this new scheme and to adopt it as the basis for his large taxonomic work already in preparation (the *Règne animal*), an obvious reference to his lectures of 1807–1812.

The first of the four *provinces* or *embranchements* — the latter term was preferred — was that of the Vertebrates. Its principal characters were a spinal nerve cord or medullary cone, expanded anteriorly (brain) and giving rise to the general nervous system. There were an internal, hard, bony skeleton, always five senses, always red blood, muscular heart, and horizontal jaws. The *embranchement* was subdivided into four classes "according to the modification of the respiratory and circulatory systems."

The second *embranchement*, the Mollusks, was characterized by the possession of a distinct brain, scattered ganglia and nerves, but no central nerve cord. "In consequence," Cuvier decided, "they have no vertebral column or skeleton," another example of the deductive reasoning to which the anatomical rules were so favorable. The mollusks were further recognizable by their shell, "complete and double" circulatory system, and liver but no spleen. They were subdivided, also into four classes, by a combination of characters taken from the number of hearts, the distribution of the nervous system, and the external form.

The third *embranchement*, the *animaux articulés*, possessed a very small brain but two distinct ventral nerve threads united by serial ganglia. These were the cause, Cuvier believed, of the articulates being meristic: with this special innervation, the muscles of each segment formed a separate unit. One recalls also that each segment can more or less preserve a separate existence. This is also the *embranchement* where the "passage from the presence of circulation to its absence" is observed. Where the circulatory system was seen to diminish, the trachial apparatus became more evident.

The final *embranchement*, the *zoophytes* or *rayonnés*, is considerably less convincing. Radial symmetry was its primary characteristic, but this could be meaningfully applied only when nerve material was present. That this was not always true Cuvier showed by declaring that it is in this *embranchement* that the fusion and gradual disappearance of the specialized structures into the "general mass" of the body is observed. Some of the four classes did possess reasonably distinctive features. The echinoderms, for example, had a system of closed (circulatory?) vessels and also organs of respiration, and these had to serve as the secondary range of characters.

One peculiar feature of the classification adopted in 1812, which disappeared in the *Règne animal*, is its apparent symmetry. Cuvier was particularly satisfied to have found such a harmonious assembly of zoological groups, four equivalent *embranchements* each containing four classes. The new system provided the perfect remedy for previous unbalance, and all was due to the recognition of the genuine complexity and refinement of the invertebrate organisms. The memoir of 1812 was only an introductory statement of Cuvier's complete taxonomic system and as such could safely be an oversimplified presentation. There was no longer a plea for general symmetry in the *Règne animal* for the simple reason that it was immediately denied by the species themselves. The four *embranchements* remained, but even in the well-known group of the vertebrates symmetry was lost when the class of the reptiles was later divided into reptiles proper and amphibians. Although the abstract formulation of a symmetrical classification may have contributed to the initial conception of the idea of the four *embranchements*, it never became an encumbrance to practical taxonomic work and immediately disappeared from Cuvier's theoretical discussion.

The *Règne animal* contained no novelties from the viewpoint of theoretical principles. It was the great compendium of zoology toward which Cuvier had been working since his days in Normandy. The essays of 1795 and the *Tableau élémentaire*, then the lectures of 1807–1812 extending Virey's conceptions, and finally the memoir of 1812 had sufficiently established his general views on taxonomy. The *Règne animal*, despite its size and restricted popular appeal, was reissued more often and was more frequently translated than any other of Cuvier's works, with the possible exception of his essays on the earth's history. In neither edition published during his lifetime did Cuvier prepare the volumes devoted to the insects (volume 3 of the 1817 edition and volumes 4 and 5 of the

1829 edition). This task was confided to his long-time friend, Pierre André Latreille (1762–1833), orphan, priest, master entomologist, and recipient in 1829 of one of the chairs that became available at the *Muséum* when that of Lamarck was divided. And while the number of volumes increased enormously, the basic form was not altered. One not inconsiderable merit of the work was its durability. Whatever may have been its theoretical limitations or illusions, Cuvier's *Règne animal* was beyond all question the greatest body of zoological facts that had yet been assembled.

The *Règne animal*, while conceived within the limits and illustrating the ideas of these earlier works, had another task. It was to be a logical and complete exposition of all known animals. It was not what is today called a taxonomic "key" and only in final desperation would a reasonable man turn to it in search of the identity and name of a specimen which he possessed. On the contrary, the experienced naturalist used Cuvier's work in order to gain more profound knowledge of a specimen, or a species, or any zoological unit whose identity he already knew. Using the index or his knowledge of the plan of the work he could turn, for example, to a detailed description of the elephant or to a discussion of the structure and habits of the various mollusks. A conscientious student employed the work in order to learn the general plan of the animal kingdom and the detailed structure and behavior, as far as it was known, of each animal species. The enormous difference separating Cuvier's work, its intention and its content, from those of Linnaeus and his followers should be recalled: the one was a detailed, encyclopedic review of an entire organic kingdom, the other was principally an extremely clever and elaborate system for the identification of animals. The one could by no means wholly exclude the other, although in fact Cuvier and his contemporaries possessed the advantage of greater and more reliable factual information.

The very conception of the *Règne animal* was such that, in its time, it could not possibly have served as a practical taxonomic key. Cuvier in 1817 had advanced far beyond his earlier views on the relative merits of the artificial and natural methods of zoological classification (see Chapter I). In 1790 he had written to his friend Pfaff that the first rule of taxonomy was to group characters which could be precisely described and which were of sufficient complexity to provide many supplementary features. In the *Règne animal* he spoke not of the convenient artificial system but of a "perfect" natural method as being the "ideal toward which natural history must tend." Quite obviously zoology was still far from attaining this goal, yet this was really no basis for despair since each new contribution to taxonomy brought nearer the desired goal. The natural method was the "entire science and each advance brought the science closer to its aims." [21] These familiar truisms contributed little to the general understanding of a natural system of classification except to reinforce the necessity of concentrating attention upon the animal in all of its aspects and of avoiding repetition of previous taxonomic practices which had confined attention to separate and arbitrary characters.

Only once did Cuvier devote extended discussion to the problems of the artificial and natural classifications and even in this fragmentary sketch the discussion is summary rather than exhaustive.[22] The natural system is here represented as a series of taxonomic categories each of which collects into "one category all those creatures which resemble one another more than they resemble any organism in another category of the same level." The important feature of Cuvier's conception of the natural system of classification is the fact that it was guaranteed by the principle of the correlation of parts. The principle insured the distinctness of each animal or group and thereby proved that presumably intermediate forms could not and did not exist. The subordination of characters could also be applied to the determination of the various zoological taxa, a task which it shared with a posteriori methods, that is, with direct observation. This sketch makes clear that Cuvier's highest regard was for the "generalizing" activities of the naturalist. Not only were brevity and clarity thereby introduced into natural history, but the actual order of animals in the creation was accurately reproduced.

The basic presupposition of this practice was that each kind of animal in nature enjoyed an individual identity. Each was a unique complex of morphological resemblances separated by unmistakable gaps from all other forms. Cuvier believed that the zoological species were real, in a literal sense of the word. The "natural" system was merely an intelligent ordering of the zoological *types* so as best to preserve the "real" order of nature. The *Règne animal* may thus be described as an attempt to formulate a natural classification. Cuvier's example proves that it was in no way necessary to believe in a genetic relationship between the innumerable animal species in order to present a classification of these creatures which would respect their resemblances and dissimilarities. The correspondence later developed as a consequence of evolutionary theory between the relationships of contemporary organisms and their phylogenetic history offered an explanation of these relationships which has led to a more profound understanding of the forces and pattern of nature. Whereas the merits of a "natural" system of classification are today judged by its approximation to the known genetic history of each major and minor taxonomic category, in Cuvier's mind the prominent feature in the history of each group was not change but stability. Hence a "natural" classification to him was concerned only with the systematic distribution of existing or extinct forms and was not obliged to take into account the possible connections and transformations between the two.

The four *embranchements*, expressed in terms of the *types*, are perhaps the most familiar feature of the Cuvierian classificatory system. To declare today that they are inaccurate is really a minor objection. In 1812 they constituted an enormous advance in the classification of animals. Cuvier's work, with that of Lamarck and many others, meant the beginning of the recognition of the diversity and singularity of the nonvertebrated animals. The vertebrates, particularly man and the mammals, could no longer legitimately be regarded as the model or ideal plan of construction for

97

the entire animal kingdom. Cuvier's four basic plans were, moreover, the ultimate representatives at the upper end of the taxonomic hierarchy of quite another dogma, and one which underlay his entire contribution to animal classification. This dogma, the *type* concept, was one of the cornerstones of his entire zoological philosophy.

The type concept

The idea of a biological *type* already possessed a long history when Cuvier became its most distinguished and ardent modern exponent. Philosophically it had roots in the Platonic theory of Ideas and had long played an important role in Western intellectual history. In natural history, thanks to the need for the identification and distribution of species into discrete units, to the study of confined, relatively unvarying local flora and fauna, to a too simple idea of the reproductive gap between species, and to numerous other factors, the idea of the stability of the species and, consequently, the possibility of an exact morphological definition of the species, were never without their proponents. Indeed, the latter were preponderant in the history of biology until the nineteenth century.[23]

Cuvier, in today's Darwinian world, enjoys the dubious honor of having been the high priest of typology, and thus the champion of the fixity of species. The Darwinists are not mistaken. Side by side in Cuvier's generally conservative zoological attitudes the idea of the fixed *type* and that of the unchanging species were inseparably associated. The idea of the zoological *type* was most explicitly stated in the Prospectus (1827) to the *Histoire naturelle des poissons*, which discussed in general terms the plan to be followed in the preparation of this work. After a volume devoted to questions of nomenclature and to generalities the authors (Cuvier and A. Valenciennes) planned to begin their study with a detailed account of the common European perch. As far as was possible, the characteristics of this species would be, so to speak, exhausted. Nothing was to be omitted: internal and external anatomy, size, color, form, behavior, distribution, and synonymy were each to be reviewed. The perch would be "known" as perhaps no other species. The perch was not a fortuitous selection since the authors declared that "he who knows well the perch and all of its parts can, by assuming some differences in proportions, easily form an idea of the organization of the greatest number of other species." The description of the common perch served also as a focus for the distribution of closely related species which were more remote from the perch but were still generally similar. Several species would in turn serve as the foci (*chefs de fil*) for other series of distribution. The procedure was applicable to this entire class of the fishes: "Each genus and each subgenus will always commence with the indigenous species (when such exist) and then will follow the foreign species in the order of their resemblance. The genera and subgenera which are completely foreign will come near the genera or subgenera which they most resemble." [24] The common European perch was therefore not only the first specific "type" mentioned but also the most important one because it stood as the primary representative of the largest category of the class, the Acanthopterygians. The perch was not the unique representative of this vast group. The plan of Cuvier and Valenciennes envisaged a great number of *types*, some quite similar to one another, others almost wholly unlike. A similar procedure would also be followed for the Malacopterygians and the Chondropterygians. To know these *types* meant to know the broad framework of the classes.

Encouraged by the reception which his other taxonomic works had received, Cuvier decided to follow a similar procedure in the *Histoire naturelle des poissons*. The species and genera were considered as discrete, morphologically stable units, and therefore *types*, in the *Règne animal* and perhaps even in the *Tableau élémentaire*. In these earlier works the emphasis was naturally divided between a concern for the separate species and the elucidation of the higher taxonomic divisions of the entire kingdom. The study of the fishes, on the other hand, turned directly to the species and only indirectly

99

was occupied with the more elevated ichthyological taxa. The latter were certainly presented, but in a form which they had received when Cuvier was more concerned with them, that is, they received in 1828 the structure given them in 1817 in the *Règne animal*. If, then, he followed a "similar procedure," it was only that part which studied the species and genera which was followed.

The author's declaration of intention was scrupulously adhered to throughout the prolonged publication of the work, even in the many volumes prepared by Valenciennes alone after his colleague's death. In the *Histoire naturelle des poissons* each volume is devoted to (usually) one family and each chapter to the separate genera of the families, but the *type* concept provides the basis for this practice. The first chapter fully described the *type* genus, noting its general characters and exposing its representative species. The family was thus an array of more or less similar genera, determined by the relations — probably first intuitively grasped and then anatomically justified — of the later genera to the *type* genus. The *type* species was believed to be the most representative species of each genus.

Cuvier characterized, for example, the common European perch (*Perca fluviatilis* of Linnaeus) in the following elaborate manner: dentated preopercle, spiny opercle, the suborbital somewhat dentated, soft tongue.[25] Two pages later he expanded this schematic account by contributing details on the number of rays on the gills and in the ventral fins, the form of the dentition, the nature of the scales, and the number of dorsal fins. The chapter was further augmented by the addition of sections concerned with the geographical distribution, habits, and ecological relations of the species. This was the first and model chapter of the body of the great work on the fishes. A concise, if complicated, statement of anatomical features was the essential consideration and was followed by whatever the authors had been able to ascertain concerning the other aspects of the animal. The characteristics peculiar to the family to which the species belonged, as well as those of its genera, were abstracted from the individual studies and were presented in synoptic form at the beginning of the treatment of the relevant family; the genera and generic characters were presented there.[26]

Volume after volume of the *Histoire naturelle des poissons* were devoted to these precise, complete, and unvarying specific-genera distinctions. Laurillard's belief that the fish were Cuvier's favorite animal group is readily confirmed by the long preparation and sheer bulk of this work. He had been intently studying the group ever since his days in Normandy and had prepared his first general reviews of the fishes for the early works on anatomy as well as for the *Tableau élémentaire*. He recognized the need for a thorough revision of the class when attempting to present it coherently in the *Règne animal*. It is curious to note that this revision was undertaken (1814–1815) immediately after the enunciation of the four *embranchements*. It appears that once a satisfactory general distribution of the animals had been discovered Cuvier felt free to devote his attentions to a select group of animals and that this would naturally be the fishes. He boasted that the final product of all of this work was able, thanks to the response of foreign naturalists (among them one finds Louis Agassiz and Alexander von Humboldt) and to the efforts of French explorers and travelers, to present some 5000 species, "more than four times the number listed in even the most recent (1820) works." [27]

The zoological *type*, exemplified by the species descriptions of the *Histoire naturelle des poissons* and no less fundamental in Cuvier's other taxonomic work, rescued him from the skepticism which had marked Buffon's *Histoire naturelle*. The great mass of seemingly only slightly dissimilar animals did not compel him, as it had Buffon, to place primary emphasis on individuals. In his everyday classificatory studies Cuvier was always concerned with the species or the genus, depending upon what specimens were available to him and the degree of generality he was seeking. The individual, the "raw material" of his profession, was regarded as representative of the species. A taxonomic category was a very real entity in his mind. "Buffon," he declared, was partially correct when he said that absolute characters and sharp generic separations do not always exist, that there is no orderly means of placing them, without artificiality [*contrainte*] in our *cadres méthodiques*; but this great man has gone too far when he rejected all relationships, when he refused any ordering drawn from the resemblance of structure . . . We, therefore, will relate what nature brings together." [28]

The zoological *type*, whether as a species or an *embranchement*, was what "nature brought together." It should be pointed out that the zoological *type*, although usually associated with the lower taxonomic units (species, genus), where its association with the seeming "fixity" of the species is particularly obvious, rested on ideas which permitted its extension to other categories as well. An *embranchement*, thought Cuvier, could be as well defined and as rigorously circumscribed as a species or a genus. The families and orders were usually "unrationalized" aggregations of the two smaller units and were omitted from theoretical investigations. The word "type" was not frequently employed by Cuvier himself, although when he does use it its meaning is perfectly clear and unambiguous.[29] The very word "species," in his mind, carried the same meaning.

Taxonomic categories: a priori or a posteriori?

From the statement of the principle of the subordination of characters to the establishment of the zoological *types* the progress was direct and profound. Unfortunately, however, for Cuvier's reputation and for the ultimate success of his ideas, this advance was not altogether consistent. Among the first to draw attention to the difficulties of Cuvier's system was the perceptive T. H. Huxley, who, although a fervent Darwinian, still could recognize the value of Cuvier's work and refused to contribute to the abuse which Cuvier attracted after the publication of the *Origin of species*. Huxley showed that although such "natural groups" as deer or goats could be given a definition in terms of the "co-existence" of certain parts, this would merely be "one way of stating certain facts." "It is merely another," he then added, "if we say that it is an empirical law of existing Nature that such and such structures are always found together; and that when we meet with one, there is *prima faciae* ground for suspecting that the others are associated with it." [30] Huxley's critique returns one to the foundation itself of Cuvierian taxonomic theory and practice and raises again the question of which shall be primary — morphological constancy or functional importance. Huxley's query was taken up, although not, it appears, directly, by Henri Daudin, who decided very definitely that Cuvier had developed numerous curious anatomical generalizations but that, in practice, his classifications were almost exclusively the products of morphological constancy and not the dictates of functional importance. Daudin's thesis is admirably documented. He quotes Cuvier arguing for the use of constancy and then against its use, he insists upon Cuvier's orientation toward the *école des faits* and away from the *école des idées*, and, most effectively, he is able to show without great trouble that, whatever may have been the means actually used to establish the zoological classes, from *embranchement* to species, the method followed was *not* that anticipated by the two anatomical rules. Intuitive recognition of species met either in the laboratory or in the field Daudin believed represented more accurately Cuvier's procedure, and very probably this was the manner in which the *types* were created.[31] Certainly none of the specific definitions given by Cuvier can be rigorously deduced from the subordination of parts, no matter how clever the naturalist and how convenient and arbitrary the postulates.

Daudin's analysis seems nevertheless an inadequate representation of Cuvier's complete zoological philosophy. In concentrating upon the naturalist's resolution of the zoological classes, he was led to neglect the other themes of Cuvier's work. His analysis is given over far too much to the doctrines of positivistic philosophy and from this results an almost total unconcern for the philosophic positions adopted by Cuvier himself. Furthermore, if one wished to study Cuvier's thought on the bases of only one aspect of his work, anatomy and not zoological classification (or geology) must be selected as it was not only the most cultivated but also the preferred science of Cuvier, and it provided, he believed, the foundations for his classifications of the animals.

In practice Cuvier never ceased to insist upon the primacy of the facts; they were the ostensible bases of his scientific method. But to pretend that they constitute the totality of his efforts, as Daudin has done,[32] is to ignore completely the thought and care which was lavished upon abstract ideas, upon the conditions of existence and upon the two anatomical rules. It has been seen that these ideas, correctly or incorrectly, obtusely or objectively, appear at the center of the Cuvierian zoological philosophy. They will soon be encountered again being invoked in the reconstruction of fossil animals. Since they do therefore exist, and to diminish or to neglect their presence or importance to the advantage of a not wholly satisfactory alternative would be deliberately to confine one's interest in the Cuvierian doctrine to predetermined and not necessarily accurate limits, it has been both necessary and legitimate to inquire into Cuvier's use of these ideas and to seek the reasons for which they were adopted.

Recapitulation

The nature and use of Cuvier's anatomical rules require only a brief recapitulation. Cuvier expressed the conditions of existence in the principle of the correlation of parts, a rule which emphasized the wholeness and functional integrity of the organism. It permitted what he believed was genuine morphological prediction, the results of which were assured by the certainty of physiological correlations of every major organ in the body. The subordination of characters taught that certain organs or organ systems were more important in the animal economy than others. The nervous system, the organs of locomotion, and those of nutrition occupied a scale of decreasing importance and upon this scale Cuvier had attempted to erect his theoretical principles of a hierarchical system of zoological classification.

The importance of the principles appears to lie quite apart from their particular content as specific anatomical rules. In Cuvier's opinion, anatomy was not to be left to the mercy of an undigested mass of information. An isolated fact, he believed, possessed merely a partial value and its real significance appeared only when it was integrated with all other relevant facts. The anatomical rules effected this integration and led to the ordering of zoological facts. The correlation of parts, the subordination of characters, and their underlying principle, the conditions of existence, were therefore, in the anatomical and zoological domains, Cuvier's response to his earlier plea for a rational system of nature subject to law. For Cuvier the anatomical rules were not, as they seem today, a speculative superstructure imposed upon his facts. Quite on the contrary — and in this he believed he had accomplished a major advance on the crude notions of Aristotle and Buffon — they were thought to be strictly empirical rules. They were to be nothing more and also nothing less than generalizations shrewdly drawn from the empirical evidence of natural history. Daudin's survey shows how specious this argument really was but, after having demonstrated that these abstract rules played at best a very small role in Cuvier's taxonomic practice, he failed to render justice to the part which they did play in Cuvier's zoological philosophy. Daudin ignored the importance of the fact that what Cuvier believed he was doing was as significant as the actual systematic procedures which he followed.

Cuvier's new classification of the animals had several consequences. Although subject to modification almost from its first proposal, his classification provided a new basis for the recasting of zoological taxonomy and permitted, in an era of intensive exploration and collection, the accurate identification and concise description of the growing number of novel specimens. This was true despite the fact that it was soon clear (to all but Cuvier) that there were many more than a mere four general zoological *types*. The *type* concept, certain of the existence in nature of concrete, real zoological units, remained an extremely practical tool for the systematization of the animal species. The *type* concept furthermore gave Cuvier his fundamental argument against the idea of a scale of being (see Chapter VI). Finally, the new system of classification gave a reasonable assurance that the overwhelming majority of the various kinds of animals living on the earth were known and that their taxonomic relationships were determined. Provided with this knowledge, Cuvier was able to compare confidently the animals of the present with those of the past periods of the earth's history. This comparison of the structural elements of the different specimens, theoretically founded on the two anatomical rules, was to become the principal procedure in the reconstruction of the history of life upon the earth. Comparative anatomy and zoological systematics were thus the necessary introduction to the science of the earth. Had not Cuvier first been an anatomist, it is most unlikely that he would ever have turned to the problems posed by the fossils buried in the strata beneath the surface of the earth. Paleontology, it will be seen, was for Cuvier the zoology of the past.

V

The Study of Fossil Organic Remains

*You contemplate a history of the fossil
mammals — what an undertaking! These
are the ruins of animal organic Creation
whose debris and fragments are often inexplicable but whose traces go back to the
greatest antiquity of the globe.*

— A. G. CAMPER

*My collections of [fossil] material in-
crease daily and I hope to be able to prepare from them a truly classic treatise in
this important matter.* — CUVIER [1]

N EVER before had an experienced anatomist so thoroughly studied the remains of extinct vertebrate animals. Cuvier's plan was to
use fossils as his guide in the exploration of the remote ages of the
earth's history. Fossils were to be the substance of paleontology and
the key to the study of geology.

It was necessary first to learn how to reconstruct a reasonably
complete animal from fragmentary and mutilated osseous debris.
Cuvier proposed the principle of the correlation of parts as the theoretical basis of this work, but in practice he relied heavily upon
direct (and indirect) comparison of the ancient pieces with those

from similar modern animals. The completed reconstructions disclosed that the fauna of the earth had rather frequently suffered extensive destruction. The distinct historical sequence of fossil vertebrates was then found to have been paralleled by a series of well-defined, dissimilar geological strata. Speculating upon the possible causes of these phenomena, Cuvier decided that they had evidently been produced by violent, sudden, but not universal inundations. Water had altered the appearance of the earth's surface and had destroyed innumerable different kinds of animals. The rigorous exploitation of the newly discovered union between zoology and geology was perhaps Cuvier's greatest contribution to the study of fossil organic remains. His advocacy of geological catastrophism should not detract from the scientific merit and historical interest of his work. His writings were among the first major essays in the emerging science of paleontology and they served both to motivate and to direct the extensive future development of the science.

The early French editions of Cuvier's general geological treatises were quickly followed by translations into other European languages, especially into English. The first English edition appeared in 1813, but one year after the original issue. This translation, made by Robert Kerr, was due particularly to the urging of William Jameson, a militant Wernerian geologist and perhaps the foremost advocate in the British Isles of catastrophic neptunism. It should be noted at the outset that this translation, although generally faithful to the original, committed a grave error in entitling the work *Essay on the theory of the earth*, an error which has persisted in the majority of references in English to Cuvier and his work. The original French title, certainly not chosen fortuitously, was simply *Discours préliminaire*. In 1821 the *Preliminary discourse*, in moderately altered form, acquired its definitive title, *Discours sur les révolutions de la surface du globe*. Cuvier doubtless felt that a specific reference to a theory of the earth not only was unnecessary, but could easily endanger the sympathetic reception of his work. The eighteenth century had been plagued with innumerable "theories," of which the most famous was that by Buffon (1749). To offer to the public, in 1812, a first statement of what would necessarily appear to be merely another geological adventure would have indicated singularly poor judgment. No such mistake was made; by the 1820's, whatever title was adopted, the *Discours* were a success. Cuvier never complained about the English title, but he also never employed its French equivalent. Both essays were *Discours*, the one literally *préliminaire* and the other an exposition of specific phenomena, the revolutions on the surface of the globe. By 1830 the work had been translated into German and Italian and an American edition (1818) had appeared reprinting the Kerr-Jameson edition.

The clear, unelaborate prose, so typical of Cuvier's writings, and the direct argument undoubtedly contributed greatly to the success of these works. How different they are from the two essays on the history of the earth written by Buffon; the ones factual and precise, and convincing; the others eloquent and diffuse, and stimulating. Upon finishing a reading of Buffon, the modern reader recognizes that many questions have been posed but few have been answered. Cuvier too posed questions, but no reader can doubt that he had ready his answers. And, in place of those which he did not possess, he offered few hypotheses. Although Buffon's *Epoques de la nature* (1778) and Cuvier's *Discours* are conspicuously similar in the arbitrariness of their intentions, there is an enormous difference in their mode of argument. Perhaps the principal cause of this difference is the novelty of the material with which Cuvier was working. The evidence drawn from the fossil quadrupeds was naturally his guide; he had not only reconstructed but discovered several specimens of them. A new world had been disclosed, a world no longer existing but nevertheless one whose fauna could be, so to speak, revived and classified. Balzac, in *Le peau de chagrin* (ed. 1925, p. 24), sang forth in praise of Cuvier and his triumphant science:

Have you ever been cast forth into the immensity of space and time while reading the geological works of Cuvier? Carried by his genius, have you soared over the limitless abyss of the past, as if supported by the hand of an enchanter? Discovering from period to period, from bed to bed, in the quarries of Montmartre or the schists of the Urals, animals whose fossilized remains belong to antediluvian civilizations, the mind is terrified to perceive the billions of years, the millions of people that the feeble human memory, that the indestructible divine tradition, has forgotten, and from which the heaped up cinder which is the surface of our globe, forming there a foothold on the earth, gives us bread and flowers; is not Cuvier the greatest poet of our century?

But the vigorous style and the great new wealth of zoological and geological evidence do not fully explain the success of Cuvier's *Discours*. What attracted the nonspecialist was the breadth of the subject and the implications of its results. Cuvier spoke of revolutions, of deluges (but not of the Deluge), of long-extinct species, of the newness of man on earth, of geological and civil-religious history, and of a multitude of related subjects. Bold or less cautious men could and did extend these ideas far beyond their original statement and, of course, Cuvier was not unaware or wholly displeased that his work should become a text lending support to the Christian interpretation of the origin of the present surface of the earth and of the origin and destiny of mankind. Furthermore, in no other writing is Cuvier's penchant for the cautious statement of well-considered conclusions more evident and in this, at least, he had advanced beyond his many more enthusiastic predecessors, beyond De Maillet and the abbé Pluche and beyond Robinet and Buffon.

Geology and Cuvier's geological studies

The science of geology had acquired by the end of the eighteenth century a great body of factual information and an explanation or, unfortunately, two opposed explanations for the forces of geological change.[2] The second half of the century had been exceptionally rich in descriptive geological field work. P. S. Pallas separated the Primary, Secondary, and Tertiary rocks of the Ural Mountains and generalized his discoveries for the formation of other mountain chains.

J. E. Guettard revealed the laval nature of the terrain in the French *Massif Central* and N. Desmarest later showed, in the same region, the igneous origin of basalt. German observers, especially J. G. Lehman, concentrated upon the description and classification of sedimentary rocks. The region of the Alps and the Jura had been closely examined and described by H. B. de Saussure and J. A. Deluc. One peculiar merit of these men, with the significant exception of Deluc, was their attempt to avoid speculation on geological causes. Certainly each had his particular preferences — Pallas favored a gigantic flood racing across Russia from the southeast, that is, over the Himalaya Mountains! — yet to none can the historian assign a new general "theory of the earth" or universal geological explanation, produced in the manner of de Maillet or the English diluvialists. "Buffon alone," Cuvier declared with some exaggeration (IFFC 103, *2ᵉ leçon*), "excited men to meditate upon these great questions."

Some might believe that meditation was too mild a term to designate the activities of the school of A. G. Werner, professor of mineralogy in the mining school of Freiberg in Saxony. The Wernerian school, the neptunists, taught that the three basic formations — the primary rocks, including granite and gneiss, the transition beds, composed of schists and gypsums, and the sedimentary deposits, where one found not only calcareous rocks but also basalt — were all laid down by chemical precipitation in the primitive sea. The latter two formations, plus the recent alluvial deposits, contained petrifactions. Volcanic rocks were of minor importance and limited extent. Actual geological agents, wind, water, tides, volcanos, and so on, could only very slightly affect the original precipitated strata and certainly they played no part in the formation of these strata.

The opposing school and that upon whose doctrines modern geology has been erected found its first general statement during the final decades of the century in the works of two Scottish geologists, James Hutton and John Playfair. Their doctrine, called vulcanism, stressed the igneous forces of nature. Volcanos and other igneous phenomena, wind, rain, and ice, rivers and the sea could each, over a sufficiently long period of time, profoundly modify the rocky strata of the earth. Some of these strata were formed by sedimentation, others by the cooling of molten masses; heat and pressure were, in Hutton's opinion, the essential orogenic agents. Within this vulcanist system Hutton and Playfair also called attention to the action of contemporary geological forces. Finding no reason to believe that these forces were less active in the past than they were at present, they attempted to explain the present condition of the earth's surface by the slow but regular action of known geological forces.

The neptunian system remained the predominant geological doctrine until at least the end of the century. In spite of the conversion to plutonism of two of Werner's finest students, L. von Buch and J. F. d'Aubuisson, the theory of a wide-spread sea as the principal effective geological agent, supported in England by William Buckland and in France by Cuvier, was destined to live for several more decades. Cuvier, whose German education had included the principles of mining and the study of minerals, was well informed on the subject of neptunian geology and it is easily understandable that the greatest single influence on his geological thinking, the ideas and observations of Jean André Deluc, should have been classic examples of neptunism.

Cuvier's geological researches had begun, once again, in Normandy. It was in 1792, he recalled (IFANF 2598(3), f. 21), that there clearly came to him the two guiding principles of his scientific career, rational anatomical investigation and the necessity of studying the fossil record with anatomical tools. He had at that time, he added, just discovered some fossil specimens of *Terebratula*, a small invertebrate. His first paleontological work, the famous memoir on the fossil and living species of the elephants, was read at the Institut on the 21st of January 1796 (publ. 1799), less than a year after his arrival in Paris. From this essay dates the long series of studies, published in the *Mémoires* of the Muséum, which would ultimately be collected and published as the *Recherches sur les ossemens fossiles* (1812). Recognizing the need to correlate zoology and geology, he had begun in 1806 to make long exploratory stratigraphical expeditions with his friend Alexandre Brongniart, mineralogist and later director of the royal porcelain factory at Sèvres. The two naturalists covered a great network of direct lines laid across the Paris region, an area which they gave its present name, the *Bassin parisien*, in the collaborative volume which summarized their findings. In addition to his paleontological and stratigraphical investigations, Cuvier had also shown an interest in mineralogy and crystallography. He had attempted, while in Normandy, to calculate the formulae of crystals and corresponded with the *abbé* Haüy on this problem. Although he never published any discoveries in this subject, the notes from this arduous geometrical early work disclose how familiar he was with the efforts of the new school of French mineralogy led by Romé de l'Isle and the *abbé* Haüy.[3]

Undoubtedly Cuvier's attention was early attracted to the dynamic problems of geology. In April 1797 he received a detailed account of Pallas' speculations from his Hamburg friend, J. A. H. Reimarus, the latter agreeing that the climate had changed radically and that the previous residents of the Cannstatt area had perished by inundation. Camper's letter already quoted demonstrates clearly that already in 1799 Cuvier was contemplating a natural history of extinct quadrupeds which would attempt to present the philosophical implications of their extinction and rediscovery. His first series of lectures on geology were delivered at the new Lycée in Paris in *an* XIII (1804–1805), but there unfortunately remains from this *cours* only a list, very roughly sketched in Cuvier's hand, of eight primary "propositions" with neither elaboration nor notes (IFFC 111). The following year he had the opportunity, when charged by the Institut to report on a memoir submitted by André Chrysologue Gy, to develop at length his views on the present situation in geology and on the program which the science must henceforth follow. The report was signed by Haüy and Lelièvre as well as by Cuvier, but the latter was its author and its reader before the Institut. Finally, in 1808, he began the famous *cours de géologie* delivered at the Collège de France. The material collected for these lectures served, with much modification and omission, as an essay for the *Discours préliminaire*, published only four years later.[4]

One can therefore conclude that the principal period of Cuvier's geological investigations lasted from 1796, the date of the memoir on fossil elephants, until 1808, the year of his *cours* at the Collège de France, and that after the lectures on comparative anatomy had been completed he was able to work almost exclusively on his geological researches. Hence, the surveys made with Brongniart, the *cours* at the Lycée and then at the Collège de France, the report on Gy's memoir, in addition to continued intensive investigation of the fossil quadrupeds, especially those from the gypsum of Montmartre, which date from the years 1804–1808, are the product of the most intensive activity which Cuvier ever dedicated to geological questions. The *Discours préliminaire* is merely a concise and eloquent exposition of already familiar ideas and in its definitive form, the *Discours sur les révolutions de la surface du globe*, it was enlarged but not revised. Only the sections on religious and civil history and the catalogue of fossil species were significantly expanded and the discussion of man recast. The central argument and its supporting evidence remained unaltered. Cuvier's geological ideas in 1830, the date of the last edition of the *Discours* published during his lifetime, were precisely those which he had expressed twenty-five years earlier.

Geology, fossils, and the earth's history

Cuvier's great activity and interest in geological questions did not make him a geologist. His geological studies were directly inspired by their relevance for the explanation of the fossil record preserved in the secondary and especially the tertiary rocks. Although the author of two *Discours* in speculative geology, Cuvier was a paleontologist, perhaps the first to deserve the name, and not a geologist. It may be observed that the term *géologie*, clearly defined in its modern sense by the end of the seventeenth century, began to enter into common usage in France only after 1830 (Birembaut, note 2, p. 1116). *Paléontologie* was a nineteenth-century invention and the word was not currently employed in Cuvier's lifetime. For the sake of convenience and simplicity, however, both terms will be employed here.

By the year 1800 there was no longer any question, among serious naturalists at least, that the "formed impressions" which for centuries had been discovered buried in the rocks were the remains of once-living creatures. Even diluvialists such as the *abbé* Pluche did not deny this and argued that fossils were the remains of organisms lost in the wreckage left by the great Deluge. De Maillet and Buffon concluded that the fossils were the record of a long series of historical events. Cuvier quickly and decisively disposed of this problem by remarking that, to his satisfaction, "the time is past when ignorance could maintain that these remains of organized bodies were simple *jeux de la nature*, products conceived in the womb of the earth by its creative forces." In 1808 he had argued that texture, chemical composition, and close analogy with living forms proved that fossils could no longer be considered spontaneous productions of nature (IFFC 103). This conclusion, which subsequent work has done nothing but confirm, was the essential proposition of his entire paleogeological system. He advanced, as Marcellin Boule suggested, from zoology, his first base, to paleontology and finally to geology, his weakest and most unoriginal contribution. Paleontology was nothing but the "zoology of the past." Mineral deposits, sedimentary strata, and rocky mountain ranges all contained a lesson in the history of the earth, but their teachings were distinctly inferior to those which may be learned by reading the fossil record. "How could one fail to see," Cuvier asked, "that to the fossils alone is due the birth of the theory of the earth; that, without them, one would perhaps never have dreamed that there could have been successive periods in the formation of the globe and a series of different operations?" [5]

Minerals had long formed the basis for the identification and classification of geological strata, particularly as these disciplines were followed by the Wernerian school. The works of Giraud-Soulavie in France and William Smith in Great Britain initiated the use of fossils as reliable indicators of the different strata. These two methods provided Cuvier, who was himself the unchallenged master of the second, with a convenient division of the geological sciences. The first division, *géologie positive*, was in his opinion as valid as any other observational or experimental science because it depended uniquely upon the facts. On the one hand it studied the deposits, geographical distribution, and origins of the minerals and on the other it was concerned with the anatomical and geographical relations of fossil animals to analogous living species and with the horizontal and vertical relations of the fossils with one another and with their mineral beds. This study of fossils, and not that of the minerals, Cuvier believed had led to the second geological division, *géologie explicative*, a discipline seeking to explain these facts but not noted for either its unanimity or its success (IFFC 103, *1e leçon*).

One easily deduces from this argument that Cuvier believed the dichotomy was probably a logical and not necessarily a real one. Geological speculations unmistakably annoyed him and his review of previous geological systems discovered none which were generally acceptable. Nevertheless, human curiosity being what it is, he felt that they were inevitable and that it was therefore wise to investigate the causes of earlier errors and to use this knowledge to attempt to avoid their repetition.

Previous explicative geologies had failed because they had not "taken into consideration all of the conditions of the problem." Occupied with explaining the changing level of the sea or the occurrence of tropical species in the arctic zone, they had exhausted on these questions all the "forces of their mind" and were reduced elsewhere to speculation. It was necessary first to pose clearly all of the questions requiring investigation and then to proceed methodically to attempt to answer them. Nine points of study were underlined by

Cuvier in the report on Gy's memoir (pp. 422–424), five dealing with specific geological problems and four relating to the fossils. The latter four were repeated almost verbatim in the *Discours*. "Are there animals and plants," Cuvier asked,

peculiar to certain beds and found in no others? Which species appear first, and which follow? Do these two kinds of species sometimes accompany one another? Is there a constant relationship between the antiquity of the beds, and the resemblance or nonresemblance of the fossils with living creatures? Is there a similar climatic relationship between the fossils and the living forms most closely resembling them? Have these animals and plants lived in the places where their remains are found, or have they been transported there from elsewhere? Do they still live somewhere today, or have they been wholly or partially destroyed? [6]

The problem of geology was that of finding positive answers to these questions, questions which, in their very statement, sufficiently disclose the wisdom and motives of the proposed investigation of the present surface of the earth.

If fossils were the guide to the history of the earth, then the paleontologist had to select the specimens most likely to reveal the greatest amount of information. Cuvier's choice fell upon the fossil quadrupeds and this for several reasons. It was above all patently impossible for an individual to study all fossil creatures and since a selection must be made he preferred to study a small and reasonably well-known group. Certainly the quadrupeds, more than the innumerable fossil sea shells (the subject of Lamarck's paleontological studies), permitted greater ease and precision in identification and distinction between fossil and living forms. Furthermore, the fossil quadrupeds revealed the revolutions which had destroyed them. Unlike the sea shells, which could easily survive an inundation, the quadrupeds in the area of immersion would all certainly perish. The discovery of several different populations of fossil quadrupeds therefore demonstrated the occurrence of a sequence of several separate revolutions. Finally, he argued, the great unlikelihood of discovering any new major living quadrupeds (none, he believed, had been found since antiquity except in the now seemingly exhausted New World and Oceania) became especcially significant when one recognized that none of these fossil forms was precisely similar to any of the living species. This singular fact, which answered one of the primary paleontological questions, could not be due merely to chance and therefore it "must be regarded as arising from general causes, and its study as one of the most appropriate means of permitting us to trace down the nature of these causes." [7]

Cuvier's greatest contribution to *géologie positive* was unquestionably the reconstruction of the fossil quadrupeds. Buffon had also studied the fossil quadrupeds, as well as fossil marine shells, plants, and fish, and he recognized that some at least among them no longer had living representatives. By fossil quadrupeds he meant primarily the fossil pachyderms. Between the publication of his *Théorie de la terre* (1749) and its greatly altered reappearance as the *Epoques de la nature* (1778), two of the most celebrated of all fossil animals had been discovered, the Siberian mammoth and the great animal of the Ohio, the mastodon. Buffon successfully confused these two species, plus two living species of proboscidians, and, by making but one large species of what really were four, was set on the path which sought to discover the climatic changes associated with their peculiar geographical distribution. Although the remains of the "hippopotamus" and "rhinoceros" had also been found, he remained convinced that the first quadrupeds were either elephants or elephant-like animals, and he added the unfortunate declaration that no quadrupeds were to be found in the calcareous deposits.[8] One can imagine his surprise had he been able to examine the great collection of Tertiary fossil quadrupeds which later contributed so greatly to the reputation of Cuvier. The fossils were but one of the monuments of the previous condition of the earth and were not systematically exploited by Buffon. Their number was still small, their relations to the geological strata were unclear, and no sufficient technique had been discovered which permitted accurate reconstructions based upon scattered, broken, and incomplete fossil fragments. P. S. Pallas (1769) had elaborately discussed the fossil elephants of Siberia which had been his discovery. Daubenton (1762) had applied his anatomical knowledge to the fossil quadrupeds. Camper *père* had communicated to Pallas his views on the loss of species through catastrophes (1787). No one, however, had undertaken a deliberate and thorough review of the entire range of fossil quadrupeds and at the same time earnestly searched for additional specimens. Cuvier's memoir of 1796, which did precisely this, might therefore reasonably be considered as the first truly paleontological memoir on the vertebrates ever written.

Anatomy and fossil reconstruction

In dividing the elephants into four species, Cuvier had followed an anatomical procedure. On the basis of the shape and surface of the teeth, the shape and position of the tusks, and the geometrical proportions of the crania he was able to distinguish the African from the Indian elephant and to set both apart from the equally dissimilar mammoth and mastodon.[9] Neither in this memoir nor in those which followed did he explicitly develop his procedure for reconstruction. Its general statement, although in practice it was obvious to anyone who carefully followed the reconstructions himself, was reserved for the *Discours préliminaire*, where it occupied the central position of the argument.

A new method was needed because the quadrupeds, unlike the fishes or sea shells, rarely left complete impressions in the rocks. Often only a single piece existed. Comparative anatomy was Cuvier's answer to the dilemma and the science to which he had devoted so much labor and thought assisted him in studying the fossils as well as the living animals. He recalled that "every organized creature forms a whole, a unique and closed system, whose parts mutually correspond to one another and concur toward the same definite action by a reciprocal reaction."[10] This is a restatement of the first anatomical rule which determined the correlation of all of the parts of the body. In comparative anatomy the rule had led to several important physiological generalizations. In paleontology it provided the theoretical basis for the reconstruction of the lost species. After a lengthy examination of the correlation of the parts in the carnivorous animals, always a favorite class for this kind of exposition, Cuvier concisely presented his own method:

> In a word, the form of the tooth leads to the form of the condyle, that of the scapula to that of the nails, just as an equation of a curve implies all of its properties; and, just as in taking each property separately as the basis of a special equation we are able to return to the original equation and other associated properties, similarly, the nails, the scapula, the condyle, the femur, each separately reveal the tooth or each other; and by beginning from each of them the thoughtful professor of the laws of organic economy can reconstruct the entire animal.[11]

The tone of this passage suggests a precision previously unknown in zoological activities, but Cuvier betrayed his thoughts and presented also his true procedure. It should be noted that his discussion is merely a continuation of the themes developed in the *Leçons d'anatomie comparée* and the memoirs of 1795 on zoological classification and that the criticism brought against these earlier works is equally applicable to the argument of the *Discours*. For what Cuvier acknowledged was his very real dependence upon observed correlations, to which he added an admission that the "sufficient causes" for certain correlations were still unknown (he did not admit that the causes did not exist). The naturalist, he said, must "make up for the failure of theory by the use of observation; this serves to establish our empirical laws which, when the observations have been frequently repeated, become almost as certain as rational laws," that is, as certain as the correlation of parts. The theoretical basis for reconstruction was now complete and, with the addition of this restriction upon the applicability of purely rational principles, Cuvier made his famous declaration of fossil determination, and then turned to the reconstructions themselves. His words qualify the procedure but not the confidence expressed by the passage just cited:

Now, in thus adopting the method of observation as a supplementary tool when theory abandons us, we arrive at astonishing facts. The least facet of bone, the slightest apophysis have a determinate character relative to the class, the order, the genus, and the species to which they belong; so true is this that, every time we possess merely a single extremity of a well-preserved bone, we are able, with diligence and intelligent resort to analogy and effective comparison, to determine all of these things [the other parts] as surely as if we possessed the entire animal.[12]

Cuvier, in his theoretical utterances, had confused reconstruction with identification. A single bone might permit a naturalist to identify the specimen as belonging to an already known species or genus, but only a paleontologist having long experience with fossil (and extant) creatures would be able to reconstruct the approximate form of the ancient animal on the basis of a unique piece or fragment. All depended upon experience, and Cuvier's reconstruction "principles" were really rationalizations after the fact. It must not be overlooked, however, that Cuvier himself retained full confidence in his scheme and that he considered the correlation rule a fruitful and accurate guide to the study of fossil animals.

Guettard, it seems, was the first to announce the existence of the fossil bones found in the quarries of Montmartre. Following his report (1768) several other naturalists, today quite forgotten, contributed additional summary descriptions. None of this work gave evidence that these early authors had either recognized that several species were present or had even suspected the singular nature of this material. When presented with some specimens from the area by a M. Vuarin, Cuvier himself recognized the importance of these discoveries. He began to examine attentively the specimens gathered in large private collections in Paris and also to form his own collection, which soon surpassed all of its predecessors. These specimens ultimately passed into the general collections of the Muséum, where they may still be examined today.

Although Cuvier confessed that he lacked the "omnipotent trum-

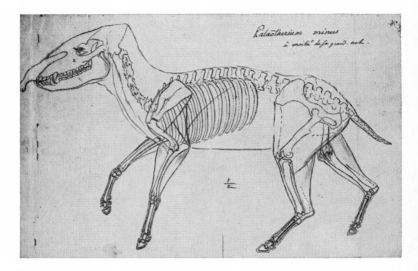

Reconstruction drawing by Cuvier of Paleotherium minus. *Since no fleshy parts had survived, the body outline was generalized from the form of the bony skeleton. Parts of the latter were also drawn from the imagination. The detail of the eye is unusual.* (MHN 625.)

pet" which could effect the necessary "resurrection in miniature," he proposed to advance with the use of anatomical laws and sound judgment.[13] One of his earliest and most successful reconstructions, that of *Paleotherium medium*, clearly illustrates his technique. A low, heavy-set mammal, the paleotherium thrived during the Eocene epoch of the Tertiary period, perhaps 15 to 20 million years ago. Cuvier found its broken remains, particularly skull fragments and the extremities of the limbs, fossilized in the gypsum deposits of Montmartre. More complete specimens were only later discovered.

The study began with a comparison of the teeth.[14] The teeth were frequently the starting point for a reconstruction since, being very hard and numerous, they were ideal material for fossilization and furthermore, in Cuvier's scheme, the shape of the tooth disclosed a great deal about the nutrition and general economy of the animal. It was obvious from the shape of the crowns of the molars that these teeth belonged to a herbivorous pachyderm. A large series of teeth was then produced and it was seen that three sizes were present. Further comparison reduced this number to two, and it was discovered that one group of molars was associated with the presence of canines, and the other group with their absence. Bringing together this evidence, Cuvier reached his first conclusion: there existed among the fossil debris from Montmartre the remains of an animal which possessed 28 molars, 12 incisors, and 4 canines (which did not protrude from the mouth). By the number of its teeth, the animal resembled the modern tapir, but the shape of its molars related it to the modern rhinoceros. No one would argue that this animal still existed on the surface of the earth; it had never been seen. Thus a new species had been discovered, a species totally unknown and completely unsuspected, and Cuvier gave to it its new generic and specific names, *Paleotherium medium*.

Assured of the reality of his new species, he proceeded to extract as much information as possible from the remains. Perhaps, since the molars of *P. medium* resembled those of the rhinoceros, the ancient animal might also have possessed a rhinoceros-like horn. The presence of small, light external nose bones, which are heavily developed in the rhinoceros, proved that the paleotherium carried no horn. Similarly, the unexaggerated intermaxillary bones of the fossil species suggested that it possessed at most a very light elephant- or tapir-like trunk. This was further confirmed by the absence of large superior maxillary nerve foramena, enormously developed in the trunk-bearing elephant. The long third and fourth *mémoires* were devoted to a similar reconstruction of the fore and hind limbs, the primary difficulty being the paucity of fossil long bones.

Cuvier had succeeded in establishing the existence of at least two previously unknown species, one of which was distinguished by the presence of canine teeth (*Paleotherium*) and the other by the absence of these teeth (*Anoplotherium*). He had in addition discovered two predominant sets of foot bones, characterized respectively by two and by three digits. The problem now was to match the two sets of heads, identifiable by their dentition, with the two sets of limbs, and thus achieve an approximate reconstruction of general body form. The most natural idea was to relate these parts in a one-to-one ratio but, since both the teeth and the feet were equally good taxonomic characters, neither could be given primary consideration and hence they were in themselves inadequate for the object assumed. Instead, it was necessary to employ either zoological *affinités* or respective size. Size gave no conclusive answers. In both sets of feet there were bones of "small horse size," yet only one head was known which was proportional to these limbs; Cuvier admitted that he had no means of assigning it to one or to the other. Furthermore, there was one leg, but two heads, of "lamb" size, one in each genus; this, also, was quite inconclusive. Then one found two "pig size" heads, one in each genus and also two proportionate tridachtyl feet, another situation which yielded no satisfaction. He then decided that it was not necessary for the body parts to be in equal proportions, as had been assumed for the preceding comparisons. The proportion between the length of the head and that of the foot is, for example, 12 to 7 in the pig but 1 to 1 in the horse. This implied that relative abundance alone might suggest the appropriate combination of heads and feet and, in fact, by assuming that *Paleotherium's* large head is associated with small feet and the small head of *Anoplotherium* with large feet, the problem was quickly solved. The greatest proportion of the foot bones of appropriate size belonged to *Paleotherium*, a tridactyl animal, while the didactyl bones were assigned to *Anoplotherium*. There were several categories of bones left over after this operation, but, since their number or condition was insufficient to yield positive determinations, they were only listed without extensive comment.[15]

Reasons "plus fortes encore" for this determination were provided by consideration of zoological affinities. The *Paleotherium* so closely resembled, in the number, arrangement, and kinds of teeth, the shape of the head, and, above all, the composition and arrangement of the tridactyl foot, the structure of the modern tapir that, exclaimed Cuvier, "no naturalist habituated to the analogies which are so constant in all organized creatures can restrain himself from spontaneously crying out that this foot is made for his head and this head for this foot." It only remained to see that the same "affinities" did not "contradict" the association of the didactyl foot and the *Anoplotherium* head (which they did not). In all, nine species of the two genera were formed, three for *Anoplotherium*, four for *Paleotherium*, and two uncertain species. After this elegant piece of work, it is somewhat disconcerting to discover Cuvier adding, probably for a possible escape from his critics, a cautious disclaimer which suggested that if an error had been made and the wrong limbs attached to the incorrect heads, the worst that had been done was to commit "an only reciprocal" exchange.[16] This possibility in no way disturbed his confidence in the procedure.

The actual practice followed by Cuvier in paleontological reconstructions, similar to that followed in the classification of animals, departed significantly from the proclaimed theoretical principles. The correlation of parts played only a very minor role in the reconstruction of *Paleotherium* and the circumstances were no different for the numerous other reconstructions. When an appeal was made to zoological affinities it was an appeal to the known structure of a modern animal, the tapir, and not to the general principles upon which the animal economy was supposed to have been established. Cuvier reconstructed his fossils not on the basis of abstract principles but by close comparison of the remains among themselves and with analogous existent forms. After having ascertained, for example, that a small fossil animal also found in the gypsum beds, the Sarigue (South American oppossum), belonged to the family of marsupials, Cuvier predicted before an assembly of witnesses that, because of the pouch which the animal had carried, there must be present a pair of internal, supporting bones peculiar to the group. There was no evidence of their existence on the surface of the fossil and it was necessary to excavate delicately the surrounding stone. In the excavation, the bones were indeed discovered. But, in spite of the many protests by Cuvier claiming a new justification of the "zoological laws," of his first principles, the fact remains that the search for the two small bones was inspired by the previous knowledge of their existence in the related marsupial animals.[17]

However equivocal may have been the method by which these reconstructions were achieved, they were the primary factual basis of the Cuvierian explanation of geological change. The *Discours* naturally did not bother to review in detail the contents of the volumes to which they were prefixed. Cuvier assumed that the serious reader would refer to the special articles themselves. The first volume was shared by the *Discours préliminaire* and a reissue of the Cuvier-Brongniart essay on the geology of the Paris basin. Volume two compared the fossil and living species of the proboscidians, the mammoths, mastodons, and elephants. The third volume devoted eight memoirs to the reconstruction of *Anoplotherium* and *Paleotherium* and associated creatures, and four further memoirs to the other fossil animals from the Paris deposits. The final volume studied the fossil ruminates, carnivores, ungulates (including *Megalonix* and *Megatherium*), and the oviparous quadrupeds. These specimens were truly international, coming from Spain, Hungary, Germany, the Netherlands, France, and Virginia.[18]

Zoological history and catastrophism

To know the fossils, Cuvier believed, was to begin to understand the history of the earth. What was most important, what was really the essential object of all of his work and "established its true relation with the theory of the earth," was to know "in which [geological] beds each species is found" and to discover the "general laws" which governed their distribution. Rigorous comparison of the fossil species with living species disclosed a very clear succession of fossil animals, a succession which corresponded almost fully with the sequence of geological strata. The oviparous quadrupeds appeared very much earlier, that is, in deeper strata, than the viviparous. These early animals, the ichthyosaurus, plesiosaurus, early turtles and crocodiles, and the great beasts from Maestricht, all more common and varied in the past than are any of the modern reptiles, were found in the various strata across Europe which underlay the broad deposit of the rough limestone (*calcaire grossier*), a deposit which, belonging to the early Tertiary rocks, became the most important chronological reference point in Cuvier's geological system. Although some mammal-like animals had been discovered in the rough limestone, there was absolutely no evidence of the terrestrial mammals before the deposits which rested above this stratum. All of the Secondary rocks were rich in shells and fishes. Cuvier therefore concluded that all of these animals, plus the oviparous quadrupeds, appeared prior to the formation (by a long-standing sea) of the rough limestone. The viviparous quadrupeds began to appear only very much later.[19]

The first traces of the latter were found in the confused strata of sands, marls, clay, and limited fresh-water deposits which followed the rough limestone. They had thus begun their existence and left their remains only after the great sea, the next but one from the present day, had retired from the continents.[20] There was a definite order discernible in the sequence of the fossil viviparous quadrupeds. The totally unknown species appeared first: it was necessary to create new genera for the *Paleotherium* and *Anoplotherium*. Mixed with these remains were the fossils of a very few creatures belonging to still extant genera and, of course, shell and fish fossils, but no longer the great reptiles. Next appeared the remains of unknown species belonging, or very closely related, to modern genera; these included the mammoths and mastodons and the rhinoceros- and hippopotamus-like animals. They were always found in loose, unconsolidated beds of transported material. Finally, the most superficial deposits, formed along river banks or in the depths of ponds and lakes, contained only representatives of contemporary species. Using these data and the table of geological formations prepared for the *Discours* (facing p. 294) by Alexander von Humboldt, one can reconstruct schematically the parallel principal geological and paleontological successions as they were understood by Cuvier (see Table 1).

TABLE I. GEOLOGICAL AND PALEONTOLOGICAL SUCCESSIONS
AS UNDERSTOOD BY CUVIER.

Period	Deposit	Fossils
Modern		
	Alluvia	Contemporary species only
	Sandstones, fresh-water deposits, loose transported terrain	Mastodons, mammoths, rhinoceros- and hippopotamus-like animals, marine and fresh-water shells and fish
	Gypsum	*Paleotherium, Anoplotherium*, marine shells and fish
	Rough limestone	First mammals, marine shells and fish
[Tertiary]		
	Limestone	Maestricht animal, marine shells and fish
[Secondary?]		
	Below the limestone	*Ichthyosaurus, Plesiosaurus* (Jurassic animals), Thuringian monitors
Primary?	Deeper deposits	No quadrupeds; only fish and shells
	Transition rocks, Primitive rocks	No fossils
Ancient		

It became a rule for Cuvier that each geological deposit possessed a characteristic population of fossils. Nevertheless, in his writings he made no attempt to draw the full stratigraphical conclusions implicit in this fact. The role of fossils as stratal indicators was to receive its unequivocal statement from William Smith in 1815 and, in France, from Cuvier's companion, Alexandre Brongniart, in 1821. The long collaboration between Brongniart and Cuvier and the nature of their work on the geology and paleontology of the Paris basin suggest, however, that the credit for the introduction into France of this idea must be shared by Brongniart with Cuvier. This conclusion is supported by the following example. Beneath the great bed of rough limestone Cuvier found a *mélange* of various fresh-water deposits, mostly clay and coal strata. These rested in turn upon the limestone formation, a widely occurring stratum running across Germany and France from Pomerania and Poland to England. Wherever this formation (or, in its absence, the associated superior fresh-water deposits) was found, so also were found, said Cuvier, the "same organized bodies." [21]

This example indicates that Cuvier's regard was not confined entirely to the Paris basin. Nevertheless, the strata of this area were of primary importance for the system of revolutions which he suggested had created the present surface of the earth, the rough limestone serving as the first great dividing point. Perhaps this limited viewpoint can be partially explained by the unique fossil wealth of the Paris basin. No other similar fossil deposits were then known, not even in Germany where Werner's students had been identifying the mineral strata for many years. Cuvier knew the geology of the Jura mountains, his homeland, and that of the Stuttgart area, of the Maestricht quarries, of parts of Italy, and of the great alluvial areas of Holland and northern Germany — all from first-hand observation. In none of these areas were there then to be found fossil deposits even approximating those of Paris. The presence of the Muséum, the active scientific life of the French capital, and the massive building projects of the Empire which required vigorous exploitation of the Montmartre quarries were all designed to confine attention to the Parisian formations. Furthermore, the history of these deposits was singularly in accord with Cuvier's own geological opinions.

The principal result of his labors had been the discovery of a new and for the most part unsuspected world. There could no longer be any question that the fossils were the remains of once living animals. Cuvier had proved that not all of these animals had lived at the same time nor had they all become extinct together. The sequence of their appearance revealed that, in the superficial strata, the fossils belonged to species or genera having living representatives whereas, as one penetrated more deeply into the crust of the earth, the fossils were found to become increasingly dissimilar to modern forms until almost all indications of generic relationship disappeared.

The facts of stratigraphy also showed that the surface of the earth had been extensively and frequently altered. At least two thick beds of limestone demonstrated the prolonged stand of primitive seas upon the present continents. In addition, great deposits resulting from immersion by fresh water were found: coal beds and widespread, loose alluvial deposits. Finally, the association of certain fossils with specific geological formations, and the parallel change of both with the passing of time, suggested that one and the same force might be responsible for the events of both the geological and the zoological past.

Cuvier's own geological system was little more than a modified and restrained neptunism, probably originally borrowed from the Wernerian school and later augmented by the writings of J. A. Deluc. Cuvier believed that the forces which had produced these changes must necessarily have been vast in extent, overwhelming in strength, and rapid in action. The debris left by the most recent revolution indicated the rapidity with which the earth's surface was changed. A revolution which could not only destroy, but preserve by instantaneous freezing, the huge beasts of Siberia was obviously of enormous strength and suddenness.[22] This same revolution and those which preceded it had also been able to overturn heavy strata and to level forests, in short, to perform any task which the geologist might wish to explain.

The insistence upon violence and speed is in part a continuation of the attack led by Cuvier against the system of present geological causes. It certainly cannot be claimed that Cuvier's catastrophism was born in ignorance of the intellectual movement in contemporary geology. Twenty pages of the *Discours* are devoted to the rejection of the various uniformitarian arguments. Rain, snow, and ice, Cuvier admitted, do attack and wear away the mountains and hills, but this argument assumed "the preexistence of mountains, valleys, and plains, in a word, all the inequalities of the world, and consequently could not have given rise to these inequalities." Sedimentation could produce no major changes in the level of the sea, whatever minor changes were known being either still in question or purely local phenomena. Volcanos, the principal factor in the Huttonian system, generated curious and extensive local upheavals profoundly changing the surrounding countryside but not, Cuvier believed, disturbing the adjacent strata. Astronomical causes such as comets or precession were equally rejected. Cuvier concluded that all of these forces lack the strength and generality which, judged by the effects, are required and that "it is in vain that one seeks, in the forces presently acting on the surface of the earth, causes sufficient to produce the revolutions and the catastrophes the traces of which its surface discloses to us." [23]

Cuvier's own idea was that the surface of the earth had been on different occasions the victim of violent catastrophes brought about by the simultaneous immersion by the sea of previously existing continental masses and the elevation of parts of the ocean floor to become the new land areas. The primitive rocks (granite) formed the framework of the earth and upon this skeleton the other changes occurred. He declared that these earliest rocks originally existed in a "liquid state" but he did not directly state that they owed their present condition to a general marine precipitation. He later reviewed the systems of Buffon (the present earth is the product of the cooling of an originally molten mass) and of Hutton and Playfair (which stressed the efficacy of present forces, including vulcanism) but again refused to state his own preferences. What is certain is that the genesis of the primitive rocks was not considered to be an important paleontological question. Not only did these strata appear to have remained since their formation unchanged relative to the Secondary and Tertiary rocks, but they were also azoic and rocks without fossils were treated by Cuvier as beyond the realm of positive geology. One could only conclude that these rocks were formed before the fossiliferous strata and that they had remained more or less unchanged except by upheavals which preceded the appearance of living organisms.[24]

The Secondary and Tertiary strata, on the other hand, offered proof of at least two, and probably more, catastrophes. The first of these corresponded to the formation of the beds of the European rough limestone.[25] At this time the sea rose over the dry land and the continents sank into the forming depths of a new sea. The one motion exterminated the great reptiles and the other, an upheaval, killed countless fish and shells. A second certain revolution corresponded to the recent formation of great superficial alluvial deposits. At this time the mastodons, mammoths, and various marine and lacustrian fishes and mollusks died. At least four other distinct successions of animals were in evidence and, although no equally conspicuous marine formations separated these groups, Cuvier circumscribed each of them by their own specific geological conditions. Table 2 summarizes these stages. This scale is merely a restatement of the table of geological deposits (Table 1) with the earth formations replaced by the revolutions which produced them.

That water was the principal agent of these revolutions was, Cuvier believed, self-evident. His familiarity and sympathy with the Wernerian system and the sedimentary nature of the deposits of the Paris basin, upon which so much of his reasoning is implicitly based,

TABLE 2. CUVIER'S SYSTEM OF ORGANIC SUCCESSIONS AND CATASTROPHES.

Organic succession	Catastrophe
	(Inundation)
Contemporary species only	
	Certain
Mastodon, mammoths, etc.	
	Probable
Paleotherium, Anoplotherium, etc.	
	Probable
First (marine) mammals, marine fish and shells	
	Certain
Maestricht animal, etc.	
	Probable
Jurassic animals	
	Probable
No quadrupeds, only fish and shells	
	?
No fossils	
	No evidence

help to explain his selection of a primary geological force. Equally if not more important, however, was his indebtedness to the geological speculations of Jean André Deluc. A member of a solid *genevois bourgeois* family, Deluc was born in 1727 and died ninety years later at Windsor in England. During his long life he had served on the Conseil de 200 at Geneva, had been Reader to the Queen of England (after 1773), and was appointed honorary professor of mineralogy at the University of Göttingen. He had occupied himself with the study of meteorology, experimenting with barometers and thermometers, but his principal scientific interest had been the investigation and description of the geology of the Alps, the details of which were published in many series of "letters," really reports of researches, which he addressed to various European celebrities.

Deluc was convinced that Buffon's notion of a cooling earth was totally incorrect and also that present causes were completely inadequate to have generated the present surface of the earth. Only a widespread sea, he believed, could have brought about these changes. This sea, rushing in on the dry land, destroyed the greatest number of the organisms living there and greatly modified the surface features of the affected terrain. Ultimately the sea subsided, retiring to caverns deep in the earth which had been excavated either by volcanic action or by the action of water, and areas of the earth's surface again became dry and could support terrestrial animals. The collapse of these caverns, during the inundation or at other times, would explain land subsidence and earth tremors.[26]

In this crude but imaginative system Deluc had not been content to consider only the fact of the most recent catastrophe (the Mosaic Deluge) but had sought in the hypothesis of the caverns its causes. The *Discours* of Cuvier never dealt with the causes of the revolutions. Their occurrence was an accepted fact and the elucidation of the sequence in which they acted was his foremost concern. In 1807, for example, he remarked that geological systems had become so numerous (at least eighty being known) that it was necessary to classify them merely in order to remember them, and that these systems represented a turning away from the real inspiration of geology, the fossils. "Geology," he complained, "has turned to seeking causes, which should really be only its final result." [27]

Deluc's final and major geological work had been translated from the manuscript into English by the Rev. Henry de la Fite in 1809. Fifteen years later de la Fite, writing from London, sought Cuvier's ideas on the date of deposition of cave fossils, a problem treated by Deluc and more recently by William Buckland, the pious geologist from Oxford. Cuvier replied to de la Fite in a lengthy undated letter presumably from the mid-1820's. Following a discussion of the cave animals, Cuvier's letter-sketch turned to the most recent revolution. Here, in what were for him not exceptionally excessive qualifications, he stated his personal opinion on the causes of this catastrophe, and also brought forth more explicitly than usual the striking parallel between this most recent inundation and the historical deluge recorded by so many ancient peoples.

Nevertheless, I believe with M. Buckland that this catastrophe is the most recent or most recent but one of those which have affected the totality or the greatest part of the globe and the one whose souvenir is preserved by nations under the name of the deluge. I also believe that it was sudden, like several of those which preceded it and if I may express myself on [its] physical causes I would say that the most reasonable conjecture was that it was due to several ruptures in the crust of the globe which changed the level and position of the seas as they had already been changed at other periods and by other catastrophes. But I must confine myself to these general terms and I present them only as the expression of a simple conjecture. To desire more precision, to attempt to explain remote causes, and, particularly, to give the how and why of each small fact would be, in my opinion, to go much further than possible given the present state of our knowledge.[28]

Deluc had thought primarily of the most recent deluge. Cuvier was concerned with a series of several floods and subsidences. He did not, however, as is clear from the above passage, hesitate to apply with qualifications the Delucian explanation to all deluges. He could furthermore afford to leave this question somewhat to one side since it did not directly concern the fossil record nor was it necessary for the study of the latter. Yet the question of the causes of the deluges was not as absent from his mind as he liked to pretend. Though he was skeptical in print and still cautious in his correspondence, his inclinations were abundantly clear, even if only indirectly.

By eliminating the possibility that present causes had been responsible for past geological changes, Cuvier had opened the desired path to catastrophism. If, he argued, in "political history past events are easily explained when one knows the passions and intrigues of his own day," such is not the case in "physical history: [here] the thread of the operations is broken; the course of nature is changed, and none of the agents that it employs today would have sufficed to produce its ancient works." [29] In spite of their inescapable violence and suddenness, Cuvier's catastrophes were not universal phenomena. Rarely was it suggested that any one inundation had covered the entire surface of the globe. This event would have been wholly contrary to a peculiar aspect of Cuvier's catastrophism, an aspect all too frequently erroneously reported. To have believed in catastrophism as a geological agent did not necessarily require a parallel belief in the separate ("special") creation of a series of distinct animal and plant populations. The *éloge* of Cuvier by P. Flourens, among its assorted errors, appears to have also given birth to that which envisages Cuvier as the great exponent of special creations.[30]

Cuvier believed that certainly during the most recent revolution and, since there was no reason against it, very probably during preceding revolutions a certain number of individuals of various species survived the disaster. It has already been noted that marine species would be less vulnerable. Terrestrial animals, too, survived and this could only mean that some portions at least of the earth remained protected from the flood, presumably by altitude. Explicitly emphasizing this point, Cuvier declared that when he maintained that "the rocky strata contain the bones of several genera and the loose beds those of several species which no longer exist," he did "not maintain that a new creation has been required to produce the species existing today." He was saying "merely that they [modern species] did not anciently occupy their present locations, and that they must have come there from elsewhere." Suppose, he continued, that New Hólland (Australia) is submerged and that all of the marsupial animals living there perish and are buried. Suppose also that at the same time a land bridge is raised from the depths of the sea between the continent of Asia and Australia (which ultimately will reemerge). Across this bridge will flow the animals of Asia, quite unrelated to the previous Australian fauna. The naturalist, knowing these recent invaders and then discovering the lost Australian species, would be thoroughly baffled by the occurrence of two such dissimilar faunas in the same region, and such in fact was the bewilderment of the real naturalist of 1812 (Cuvier) who faced an analogous situation with the various animal populations, living and fossil, of Europe, Siberia, and a great part of America. Not special creations, but migration and mutual exchange of species explained the discontinuities of the vertical, temporal distribution of animals.[31] The subject of animal geography (their horizontal distribution) was, curiously, of very minor interest to Cuvier. He was not unaware of the suggestive essays which Buffon had devoted to zoogeography but his own preconceptions about the unvarying nature of the species discouraged any general reflections on the matter. He presumably might have argued, as his entire zoological system suggests, that a given species is, with only superficial and unimportant exceptions, an unvarying entity throughout its entire range and that when a naturalist begins to suspect that he has in his hands an exception to this rule he is very probably dealing with a different species altogether.

The sequence of fossil and mineral deposits further proved that these revolutions had not been contemporaneous. No great unique catastrophic event such as the Mosaic Deluge could have been responsible for all of the changes which the surface of the earth had experienced. One of the essential aims of Cuvier's geological investigations had been to establish the chronology of these events but only in a relative, and not in an absolute, manner. The latter, he believed, given the present circumstances of geopaleontological knowledge, was impossible to ascertain. "There is," he concluded, "this complex fact [that] a series of epochs prior to the present time whose succession can be verified without uncertainty [has existed, and,] although the duration of each cannot be stated with precision, they can serve as reference points which regulate and direct ancient chronology." [32] Unlike Buffon, who in the *Epoques de la nature* had attempted to assign a definite number of years to each geological period and thus to estimate their antiquity as well as that of the globe itself,[33] Cuvier preferred to leave the origin and all but the recent and recorded past as an unsolved, if not unsolvable, problem. The one date which was certain was that of the most recent revolution. By an inversion of the uniformitarian hypothesis, which, it will be recalled, was considered inadequate to explain the genesis of marked surface irregularities, Cuvier sought to demonstrate the newness of the present continents. If, he argued, present causes are active, which undoubtedly they are, then the present surface of the earth cannot be very ancient. By estimating the present rates of erosion, sedimentation, and peat formation one could see that, given unlimited time, these forces would have completely obliterated all surface features. On the other hand, using these estimated rates, the naturalist could trace back the beginnings of alluvial deposits dropped by the Po, Nile, and Rhône, the commencement of the landward advance of the western European and African sand dunes, and the first growth of the peat beds to not more than 4000 years before our (Christian) era, that is, to not more than 6000 years ago.[34] By interpreting evidence left by the retreat of the last general European glacier as stemming from the most recent revolution, Cuvier, blatantly in error, believed that he had discovered irrefutable physical proof of the newness of the continents. It was fortunate for him that he knew nothing of the great glacial sheets which once had covered Europe and was therefore unaware that the last glaciation had retreated well before 4000 B.C. Here indeed the use of evidence from a restricted area served him poorly.

Cuvier was able to turn also to civil history for support for his thesis. The massive section in the *Discours* on the history of ancient peoples was undertaken to demonstrate that none of these civilizations enjoyed an antiquity greater than that allowed by the last reemergence of the continents. The pretended spectacular antiquity attributed by ancient historians to their own nations was, he maintained, pure myth and the product of ignorance. When the historical data become more reliable one discovers that Egypt, Chaldea, China, and India possessed civilizations which, instead of being 20,000 or even 15,000 years old, cannot be proved to have existed prior to 4000 B.C. The civilizations which then arose and flourished left, several thousand years later, various kinds of written records, among them semimythological tales of the early history of the tribe or nation. The Gilgamesh Epic from Mesopotamia was among these and, from a much later period, Cuvier cites Apollodorus, Plutarch, and Lucian. Now, he continued, one of the most striking features of these accounts was that each tells in some way of an earlier, disastrous flood: Deucalion was "given a chest for safety," Plutarch spoke of doves which sought to learn "if the waters had abated," and Lucian lists the animals which departed with him.[35] This discovery was preceded by the brief remark that the nearer the historian approaches the historical era, the more he discovers authors whose accounts more closely resemble in detail that narrated by Moses. The natural and civil history of the earth therefore concurred in giving as the date of the most recent revolution, which prepared the terrain for the development of modern civilizations, as not earlier than 4000 B.C.

Conclusion

There is little originality in Cuvier's account of the earth's history. The notions of catastrophes and migrations and the modest attempt to establish the date of the last revolution were merely the working out of previously current ideas. One feature of Cuvier's geological doctrine, however, should be reemphasized: the demonstration by comparative anatomy of the fact of organic succession.

Cuvier's paleontological studies, and those of Brongniart, Smith, and others, clearly demonstrated the significance of the geological strata for the study of the history of life on the earth. A succession of different organic *types* — the various vertebrate fossil animals — was the substance of this history. Ancient animals were discovered to be unlike modern creatures, and all ancient animals at all times were found to be not all alike. Certain kinds of animals had become extinct, others had persisted, while still others were recognized as only recent in origin. Life had indeed had a history and a history which could now be recovered.

Comparative anatomy was the science which had permitted this recovery. Whereas the reconstructions themselves were really the product of direct comparison of ancient and modern forms, the reconstruction procedure had been justified by the principle of the correlation of parts. The former gave the paleontologist his complete animals and the latter told him that his specimen was precisely as it should be. The correlation principle insured that the ancient animals would be as morphologically unique and taxonomically distinct as any modern organism. The *type* concept was therefore applicable throughout the entire succession of animals.

Anatomy, taxonomy, and paleontology were all parts of one comprehensive scientific doctrine. They were not cultivated in isolation but shared with one another a common methodological procedure and general conceptual foundation. The foremost element of this conceptual foundation was the first anatomical rule, the correlation of parts. The reconstruction of lost species and the explanation of organic structure and function could together be traced back to this fundamental principle, and the determination of the zoological taxonomic categories was theoretically derived from the corollary of this first rule, the subordination of characters. It is clear that anatomy, or, better, comparative anatomy, served always as the scientific basis of Cuvier's empirical investigations and hypothetical propositions. In practice and theory, anatomy was, as no other science could have been, Cuvier's special and unchallenged domain. The science of anatomy, furthermore, because of its pivotal position was the principal source of Cuvier's scientific opposition to the idea of the transmutation of biological species.

VI

The Species Question

M<small>ANY</small> of the problems raised by the modern theory of organic evolution were to receive Cuvier's careful attention. The extent of the morphological variability of individuals and of species, the effect of environmental influences upon organisms, the complexities of structural analogies among animals, the ancient issues of spontaneous generation and preformation, and the place of man in nature were all questions to which Cuvier addressed himself. He was especially concerned to make known the untruthfulness of the idea of a graduated scale of nature.

Despite the coherent and relatively complete recent formulation of general biological philosophies by J. B. de Lamarck and Etienne Geoffroy Saint-Hilaire, Cuvier separately and not systematically criticized those among their ideas which showed specifically evolutionary tendencies.[1] Lamarck's insistence upon the variability and transciency of species and upon the indirect but profound action of the environment (by means of induced *habitudes*) on the structure of organisms was the principal contemporary source of the transmutationist doctrines which Cuvier resisted. Geoffroy adopted and modified certain of the Lamarckian ideas but was guilty, in Cuvier's eyes, of a further heresy, the advocacy of the structural unity of the entire animal kingdom, a notion taken from the German *Naturphilosophen* and itself associated with additional transmutationist hypotheses. Cuvier found that by rejecting these special propositions he was able to repudiate also the general systems in which they were contained. Cuvier understood that questions pertaining to the nature and history of biological species were numerous and difficult to resolve. He realized that no single, simple speculative doctrine, however logically elegant and philosophically satisfying it may have been, had yet succeeded in answering these questions.

Evolution and the limits of variation

The term *transformisme* was Lamarck's expression for the process of the temporal change of organic species. It is the appropriate contemporary phrase and suggests Cuvier's counterargumentation, which will be labeled simply "antitransformism." The term "evolution" acquired its modern connotation only toward the middle of the nineteenth century and is most closely identified with Darwinian theory. For Cuvier *évolution* retained its earlier meaning: the development of the germ into the adult animal. Evolution, in its modern sense, is an ambiguous word. Like transformism it denotes both the process and the mechanism of change, each of which is different in the different systems. Although evolution is today often translated into the French *transformisme*, the two doctrines have historical associations which make it advisable in a study of Cuvier to keep them separate. Transformism was for years the label of a distinctly Lamarckian view of organic change, while the term evolution, since Darwin, has suggested the primary role of natural selection. The distinction between the two is not absolute but may be adopted for the sake of convenience. Evolution will be employed in its modern neo-Darwinian sense and therefore is not synonymous with transformism. Transformism is reserved for the pre-Darwinian period. It is the process of change and includes but is also something more than the transmutation of species.

Modern evolutionary theory postulates at least three factors essential to the transmutation of species. The populations of individuals composing the species vary — hence, we say the species varies — and are therefore differently suited for the conditions under which they must live. Secondly, it is necessary that some mechanism be available which can impose a seeming "directedness" upon the change of these varying individuals and, again, their species. Natural selection plays this role in the Darwinian theory. Finally, as it is believed that these variations are commonly very slight (although ubiquitous) and that great changes can come about normally only by their gradual accumulation, a great span of time becomes absolutely essential if these events are to take place. These requirements are common to Lamarckian transformism as well as to Darwinism. There was a great difference, however, between various features of the two theories. Random variation cannot be equated with the Lamarckian idea of induced variation, nor can the long-term indirect effects of the environment, via *habitudes*, be compared with the activity of natural selection. Directedness in one theory was due to natural selection and in the other theory was evident from the organisms attempting to ascend the zoological *série*. Time, measured in thousands or even millions of years, was a common feature of both theories.

Cuvier did not deny the existence of variation. His plan was to reduce variation to its proper limits, and the anatomical rules provided the initial key to the problem. From the primary fact of the integral harmony of the organism it was recognized that certain organs were more important to the animal than others: heart, lungs, nervous system were more important than hair, skin, color, or size. These circumstances demanded a certain stability or invariability of the central organs and permitted the almost unlimited variation of peripheral features. "Thus we find," Cuvier declared,

more numerous varieties in measure as we depart from the principal organs and as we approach those of less importance; and when we arrive at the surface where the nature of things places the least essential parts — whose lesion would be the least dangerous — the number of varieties becomes so considerable that all the work of the naturalists has not yet been able to form any one sound idea of it.

The differences between individuals of a given species were therefore numerous but of only minor functional significance. These

143

varieties undoubtedly arose from the varying conditions under which each individual had developed. Heat and nutrient supply were probably the most influential agents, sometimes modifying the entire body and at other times only the peripheral organs. But these effects were extremely vague and "differences of this kind between organisms, which are called *variétés*," must be accepted although still unexplained. Varieties were therefore "confined within very limited bounds" and no matter how far back into antiquity one explored he discovered that these limits were the same then as those of today.[2]

Under Cuvier's definition almost every individual, being somewhat dissimilar from its closest relative, could be considered a *variété*. His species definition suffered no similar imprecision. The failure of successful reproduction, that is, the production of subsequently fertile offspring, was the decisive specific character. The species was defined as an "assemblage of individuals which have descended from one another or from common parents and [also] those individuals which resemble them as much as they are similar among themselves."[3] This definition was, as Cuvier himself recognized, more verbal than real. It was all very well to declare that a fertile crossing between individuals indicated conspecificity but it was a far more difficult problem actually to produce such crosses. A passage written to Pfaff in 1790 is very revealing in this situation. Pfaff had wished to derive the numerous present races of dogs from four primitive races and solicited Cuvier's opinion on this proposal. Cuvier's response was noncommittal but skeptical.[4] He declared that he had not given an opinion on this "question of fact" because it was not yet certain "whether their different species could produce fertile offspring." He demanded a "synthetic proof" and by this he meant "the production of all of the known races of dogs from your primitive races. So long as this experiment has not been made only an hypothesis will exist." The necessity as well as the near impossibility of this demonstration were evident to Cuvier and it is perhaps for this reason that he added a morphological clause to his species definition. In practical taxonomy the tangible characters were to be the sole resort of the naturalist. The morphological definition nevertheless was considered to be absolutely inferior to that based on generation and was preferred only because of its immediate usefulness. An earlier letter to Pfaff contained the essence of all of Cuvier's speculations on the nature of the species. After setting aside "classes, orders, and genera" as "simple, human abstractions" (but each of great utility), he preached the following sermon to his friend:

But are the species simply abstractions? Does there not exist a real bond (*analogie*) by which all the individuals of a species are marked? Reflect on that! You will find that we call a species all the individuals which in fact descend from the same pair, or which at least may descend from it. We imagine that a species is the total descendence of the first couple created by God, almost as all men are represented as the children of Adam and Eve. What means have we, at this time, to rediscover the path of this genealogy? It is assuredly not in structural resemblance. There remains in reality only reproduction and I maintain that this is the sole certain and even infallible character for the recognition of a species. All other proofs are merely presumptions.[5]

Structure, varying from individual to individual, was presumably too indefinite to allow a concrete species definition (but not delimitation) and hence could serve only as one index of the species.

Cuvier believed that external agents could modify the adult organism as well as the embryo. The focus of the problem remained the extent of the variation induced and this seemed very slight indeed. Three factors might induce these mutations: climate, behavior, and domestication. Consider, he asked, the enormous differences between the habitats of the wild herbivores. Here the feeding area is rich and there it is poor, depending upon local climatic conditions, but throughout this great range of conditions we are pleased to discover that, apart from size, color, and other external features, the essential similarity of the important organs and body relations of such animals as the elephant and reindeer has been preserved.

Nature had also provided that by "mutual aversion" individuals of different species would not attempt to mate. Under special circumstances man had been able to force such matings and by domestication create apparent hybrids. Cuvier was highly critical of the results of these efforts. Indeed, Michel Adanson in the 1760's had performed several such experiments on the grains, and had produced, it seemed, two new types. Continued examination revealed, however, that the offspring were infertile and that naturalists who had pushed "these and similar facts too far, maintaining that the species are not constant," were completely mistaken. It was a fact, Cuvier admitted, that the "*dégénération* of the species goes quite far." These words show, however, that Cuvier's use of Buffon's famous term, *dégénération*, was sharply restricted. Varieties within a species he believed might arise by the action of domestication, but in no circumstances might the species themselves be altered or transformed one into another.[6]

A final agent which had been considered, Cuvier surmised, as a force of change was that rather abstract feature of the universe, time. Like the previous agent, time was wholly incapable of altering the species. Had it not been proved, he demanded, that the mummified animals brought back to France by the naturalists of the Egyptian Expedition were morphologically similar to modern forms and, since in some two or three thousand years, as far back as the evidence permitted study, the species have changed not at all, was there any conceivable reason to suppose that, given even a greater period, they would have changed? Cuvier's conclusion was inevitable. The species, the individuals of which were highly variable, were themselves highly stable units (*types*), totally separated from those animals which might resemble them by uncrossable reproductive barriers. There was a constant nucleus of specific characters which could not be disturbed. "There are, therefore," Cuvier decided, "among the animals characters which resist all influences, either natural or human, and nothing indicates that time has in their regard more effect than climate or domestication."[7]

Issues of transformism

The *type* concept served many more functions than its role as a taxonomic tool superficially appeared to suggest. On one hand, the specific *types* were invariable and hence inalterable; on another level, their clearly marked individuality prohibited the construction of unique series of increasing or decreasing organic complexity. The notorious *échelle des êtres (série)* was, in Cuvier's outspoken opinion, perhaps the gravest of all zoological errors. There are suggestions that during his youth he had given passing approval to the idea. His first scientific publication, a classification of the sowbugs, noted the "almost continuous chain" which linked the terrestrial and aquatic sowbugs with the marine mantis shrimp. He concluded with the not unfamiliar remark, "Here, as elsewhere, nature makes no leaps." [8] The outline of the preliminary discourse (1795) to his first series of anatomical lectures contained a sketch suggesting the existence of the *série* (MHN 609, *prem. partie*; see the accompanying diagram), but no vestige of this idea remained

Echelle décroissante des animaux

Polype: sa simplicité et ses facultés

in the published text. Never again did these timid essays reappear. The idea of the *série* received a fair share of some of Cuvier's most haughty abuse, particularly in the ninth chapter of the first volume of the *Histoire naturelle des poissons*. One passage alone from this chapter summarizes the opinions which he had expressed since at least 1800 (in the *Leçons d'anatomie comparée*):

It must not be imagined that because we place one genus or one family before another we would consider them as more perfect, as superior to others in the system of nature. He alone has this pretension who pursues the chimerical project of placing the organisms in a single line; we have long ago renounced this scheme. The more we have progressed in the study of nature and the more we have become convinced that this idea is one of the most untrue notions ever introduced into natural history, the more we have recognized that it is necessary to consider each organism and each group of organisms in itself and in the role that each plays by virtue of its properties and its organization, and to make no abstraction of any of their relationships or of any of the links which attach them to the other organisms, from the closest to the most remote.[9]

The explanation of this condemnation and of the reasons which brought about the doubtless slight change in attitude in Cuvier as regards the *série* is found in the preface to the *Règne animal*. He there assigned the responsibility for this great "obstacle" to the progress of natural history to the "erroneous application to the totality of creation [of] partial observations." Cuvier was not unaware that by selecting one organ and tracing it through all possible zoological classes a very clear sequence of increasing complexity, that is, "perfection," could sometimes be discovered. The procedure was precisely that upon which his great anatomical studies were established. However, the results of several different lists of organic hierarchies showed both the generality and the limits of this approach. The scale of nature was by definition a unique scale and required for its conclusive demonstration the combination of these numerous special scales. Such a measure was to Cuvier's mind as preposterous as it was impossible. To make this demonstration "we must calculate the effect resulting from each combination" and it was perfectly obvious to Cuvier that "this is impossible." The individual scale could not even be used to establish a hierarchy within each *embranchement* or between two *embranchements*. On this point there was some ambiguity. Although there could be no transition between, for example, the first and the second *embranchements* (vertebrates and mollusks), there did exist some *rapport* between the numbers and organization of the parts of members of these two groups. The cuttlefish were so complex that no other creature could "reasonably be placed between them and the fish." And within these two *embranchements* were two different "series of degradations of a common plan," that is, of the *type*, and one descended "from the cuttlefish to the oyster almost as from man to the carp." A moment later, Cuvier terminated the discussion by indicating that, from any point of view, there are four classes which belong to each *embranchement* but they do so "without forming a series or enjoying any incontestable rank." It seems that the appearance of a *série* within an *embranchement* was suggested by the over-all complexity of certain members of the group, but that further examination unfailingly showed that other, generally simpler, members possessed certain structures which were in themselves more complex than the same or similar parts in the "higher" animal, and hence, as Cuvier noted, the calculation was impossible.[10]

Cuvier preferred an image similar to that employed previously by Linnaeus. Instead of the erroneous plan of the system-makers, who wished only to place an organism "between two others," it was necessary to envisage each creature held by innumerable bonds to all of the others and thus to take into account all possible ramifications of relationship. Found "sometimes closely, other times distantly, in the great network which constitutes organic nature," the individual and the species were all interconnected, although distinct, and they would not fit even approximately into a preconceived pattern such as the *série*.[11] Cuvier did not repeat Linnaeus's map image, but his conclusion was the same: organic nature was composed of an almost numberless quantity of well-defined species, in turn similar to or different from one another and this in an enormous variety of ways. By an arbitrary selection of characters the naturalist could create the semblance of a hierarchical series of organisms, but this inevitably entailed the neglect of other equally important characters.

These criticisms were specially applicable to a *série* extended in space, that is, to the whole of a simultaneously existing creation. With the alternative proposal, a *série* or gradation of organisms having arisen during the course of an extended period of time, Cuvier had even less patience. One might even suspect that he considered the idea so absurd, or so perfidious, since it was the central point of the transformist argument, that he refused even to discuss it. Certainly his remarks concerning the temporal scale of nature are few and terse. He based his entire refutation upon the incompleteness of the fossil record. If the fossils could not show us the course of the supposed transmutations, what reason was there to believe that these unusual events had actually occurred? The fossils were our only record of life in the remote past and their lesson was obvious and not at all, Cuvier believed, what the transformists would have liked it to be. Not a continuous series of almost similar creatures but rather an interrupted sequence of dissimilar forms was what was discovered. "We may," said Cuvier, "respond to them [transformists] in their own system, that, if the species have changed by degrees, we should find some traces of these gradual modifications; between the paleotherium and today's species we should find some intermediary forms: this has not yet happened." [12] There is no reason, furthermore, why these fossils should not be found unless the ancient species were "as constant as ours" or because the catastrophes did not leave enough time for the transformations.

Time had indeed brought about a succession of life on the earth but not a succession from species to species. It is erroneous to place Cuvier without reservation in the so-called "progressionist" school.[13] Progressionism, assuming that "life has risen from simple to more complex forms throughout the successive eras of the geological past," was essentially peculiar to the English development in the early nineteenth century of the catastrophist doctrines. In Cuvier's system there was certainly no place for a progressive advance of animal organization, progress usually having reference to the degree of approximation to the structures of the "higher" animals, the mammals and especially man. One need only recall Cuvier's insistence upon the integrity and special conditions of existence possessed by every kind of creature to see that no one of them, with the possible exception of man (see below, p. 165), was superior or had "progressed" beyond the others. His system was, if anything, "extinctive," eliminating by catastrophe, and not "progressive," creating (through God) new and higher creatures as an aftermath of catastrophe. There had been a succession of discrete populations, each more or less complete, and each neatly perishing by the action of some remote catastrophe. This was demonstrated a priori — Cuvier's geological hypotheses did just this — at the same time that the succession of forms was rejected (IFFC 94, f. 340).

The *série*, in both its ordinal and its temporal forms, had been and remained during Cuvier's lifetime one of the more striking ideas which the school of *Naturphilosophie* had passionately adopted and propagandized. In opposition to the *série* Cuvier had advanced his idea of the zoological *type*. The same instrument he also used to combat another, almost equally prevalent, aberration emerging from the German philosophers and finding as champion in France Cuvier's colleague, Etienne Geoffroy Saint-Hilaire. This was the idea of the unity of the animal kingdom. "Nature," the *Naturphilosophen* had declared, "is neither the abstract unity of a concept as in mechanism nor a multitude of qualitatively distinct forms; it is a single life with multiple forms, a unique and infinitely fecund center." [14] To this kind of thinking Cuvier replied that nature, meaning of course the creative hand behind nature, was free to produce whatever was necessary for the specific needs of each individual, and if this entailed the violation of a supposed unity of organic nature then so much the worse for the latter (IFFC 94, f. 287).

Perhaps the best-known event in Cuvier's career was the debate in which he engaged with Geoffroy at the Académie des sciences (January–May 1830). The course of this debate is a story in itself and contributes little that is new to the understanding of Cuvier's anti-transmutationist position. The conflict was not, as is popularly supposed, principally between an *école des faits* (Cuvier) and an *école des idées* (Geoffroy) or between transformist and antitransformist philosophies. These elements did enter the debate, particularly from Geoffroy's side, but the central issue concerned a morphological question, the presumed unity of structure between the mollusks and the vertebrates and, later, between the several vertebrate classes.[15]

Another of the great battlegrounds over the unity of composition was the cranial structure of the vertebrates. With the work by which Geoffroy had demonstrated the very great similarity of construction between the skulls of the several vertebrate classes and furthermore had made the capital discovery of the analogy between the mammalian inner ear bones and parts of the branchial apparatus of the fish, Cuvier was fully in accord. He saw that, in its essential features, the vertebrate skull admitted "no exceptions" and that although exact similitude did not appear the same names could be applied to the similar bones throughout the entire class.[16] It was the attempt by Geoffroy and others to pursue this analogy beyond the skull which brought his prompt denunciation.

One of the favorite occupations of certain *Naturphilosophen* had been to seek a universal analogy for the vertebrates. Their choice had fallen upon the vertebra itself, which, by a singular mental exercise, was taken as the basic model for all the other vertebrate structures, great or small, and including naturally the cranium. Cuvier, to his satisfaction, demolished this scheme. The fabric of the skull, he argued, was composed principally of the basilar bone and the sphenoid complex. While it was true that the basilar is annular, possesses a central fossa, and is composed of three segments cemented together, this only proved, Cuvier believed, that it served the same function (supporting the head) as the vertebrae and was not necessarily morphologically analogous. The sphenoid complex was conclusive. It was not always annular, it was not always composed of three pieces, it was not always fully ossified and cemented together. There were furthermore secondary additions to it (parietals and frontals) which had absolutely nothing to do with the structure of a vertebra. Not only did the osteology of the skull confound the notions of Oken, Autenrieth, and Baudin, cited by

Cuvier as guilty of formulating the idea, but the muscular fabric of the foreskull was totally dissimilar to that of the vertebral column.[17]

No more could there exist anything but a very approximate unity of plan between the vertebrate skeletons. They were indeed "formed on the same plan" but this meant only that the head, lower jaw, and vertebral column were present and that variations were common among all of the other parts. Thus, man lacked a tail, the frogs lacked ribs, the serpents a sternum and sometimes all four extremities, and so on. Each class had to be considered separately and in all of its specializations (IFFC 104, *8ᵉ leçon*).

Unity was equally absent between members of any other *embranchement* and, of course, there was positively no identity of structure between any or all of the four *embranchements*. This was true for *unité de composition* (similar parts in an equal number placed in the same order in all animals), for the *unité de plan* (general, over-all similarity of all animals), and for the *unité de connections* (all parts similarly related to one another in all organisms). It was a truism to Cuvier that all animals were built upon not one common plan, but four. Each *type d'embranchement* served as the basis for many animals. Because each of these basic *types* was structurally unique, no great morphological similarity between members of two, three, or four *types* could be expected.[18] Cuvier therefore rejected the notion of the unity of animal form. Once again the idea of the *type*, a strange blend of philosophical and practical zoology, had rescued the integrity of the species, this time not from transmutation but from eventual disappearance in the great Oneness of nature. Cuvier's satisfaction was complete. He had been able to demonstrate factually the error of an idea which, to anyone who demanded a "Creator God," concerned for every individual *qua* individual in His creation, was already "perfectly ridiculous" (IFFC 94, f. 340). Ordered diversity, not unity, was the rule of organic nature.

The *type* concept moreover provided an answer to the enigma of vestigial organs. Cuvier believed that these structures were real but, on the level of philosophical zoology, irrelevant. He suspected that they were most evident among the organs of locomotion. The number, form, and composition of the digits showed all kinds of peculiar variations. Some naturalists had even suggested that vestigial organs implied the *passage* or transformation of one part into another, of feet, for example, into fins. The modern conclusion, that these rudimentary structures were indeed *passages* between organs or perhaps the terminal remains of once possibly highly developed organs, was not unknown to Cuvier and it naturally provoked his condemnation. Only by abusing the right principles of zoology, he protested, could one effect these transformations. Like the species, like the individuals, like all of the parts of an organism, the vestigial organs did exist and must therefore be studied. It nevertheless was not regarded as sound zoology to seek their origins. The vestigial organs, like species and individuals, must be accepted precisely as they were. This was not too difficult because they were believed to be quite uncommon. Cuvier, for example, had casually announced that "it is true that there are vestiges and this is one of the remarkable peculiarities of natural history," and he then had abruptly dropped the subject (IFFC 92, f. 391). The vestiges were regarded as an essential part of the Creation and therefore had their own *raison d'être* even if we were forced to remain ignorant of it. No law, Cuvier declared, could "compel the Creator unnecessarily to produce useless forms." [19] No argument was offered suggesting that vestiges or other inexplicable organs existed for the sake of the completeness or harmony of the world. Cuvier very probably considered this familiar eighteenth-century hypothesis as gratuitous and unsound. Furthermore, the infrequency and general insignificance of vestigial organs made them a really minor zoological problem.

Disputes over the zoological meaning of vestigial organs became acute only after the publication of the *Origin of species*. Another issue likewise intimately connected with the demonstration of Darwin's evolution theory became a topic of considerable debate well before 1859. This was the question of the significance and relative importance of resemblances and differences between organisms, of the analogies and homologies which might exist between organic structures. Richard Owen, anatomist, paleontologist, and first director of the British Museum (Natural History), appears to have been the first naturalist to distinguish clearly between biological homology and analogy. The fact itself of close organic similarity had been known from the earliest days of comparative anatomy. It was recognized that these similarities were of two kinds: a common structural piece (the hand, fin, and wing) and a similarity of function (the action of the wing of the bird and that of the insect). Considerable ambiguity continued to exist because similar functions could be performed by almost wholly similar parts and hence no distinction could be drawn, or very similar parts might perform quite dissimilar functions, such as is found in the developmentally similar beak of the bird, whose serrated edges serve as "teeth," and the lips of the mammal. Owen labeled parts which performed the same functions analogous and those which were morphologically identical, no matter what function they might subserve, homologous.[20] Mere definition was not an explanation of these anatomical generalizations. Owen's own brand of transcendental anatomy which explained homology as a tangible reflection of an eternal "archetype" proved unsatisfactory to experienced naturalists. Darwinism, if not Darwin himself, who appeared to be somewhat confused by this complicated study,[21] ultimately suggested the explanation still in favor: homology and analogy are both genetic products of evolution. Homology is regarded as due to common descent and analogy is not. Correct understanding of organic homology has become one of the great modern evidences indicating community of descent in the transformation of species.

Although the *Leçons d'anatomie comparée*, because of its formal arrangement, could be considered by modern evolutionists as one of the great compendia of homologies, Cuvier never really made clear what he meant by similarities. Comparative anatomy, he believed, was the science which could follow any organ through its many "metamorphoses" (IFFC 112, f. 73). But it was obvious to Cuvier the anatomist that when "nature produces resemblances from one class to another, they are only apparent" (IFFC 104, 9ᵉ *leçon*). This argument is supported by a list of flying species found within the vertebrate *embranchement*. For the mammals there is the bat, the birds are of course the model of aerial animals, the reptiles have the "flying dragon," and the fishes the "flying fish." Certainly, in this unharmonious potpourri, the resemblances were apparent only. They were not even analogous, since the possession of a refined apparatus for flying, as distinguished from gliding, was not common to all. Quite simply, for Cuvier, whatever resemblances might be found (and they were numerous) would be due to a logically prior similarity of function. "Let us then conclude," he declared, "that, if there are any resemblances between the organs of the fish and those of other classes, it is only insofar as there are resemblances between their functions." [22] From this point of view Cuvier's anatomical bias appears to be analogical, but it must be remembered that, although his principles of anatomy were developed and stated in physiological and functional terms, the actual resemblances were evidenced by practical anatomy. That the wing and arm were structurally alike was as much a fact for Cuvier as it was for any other anatomist. Cuvier's explanation for this homology was simple and has already been noted. The anatomical rules decided which organs would and which would not coexist. These rules were determinate and hence so were the *types* which they regulated. Those animals within the same, created *type* would naturally be functionally similar and therefore morphologically similar. In like manner, those outside of this *type* would be essentially different. Analogies in the modern sense (Cuvier employed the term *analogue* for *any* resemblance) could therefore be no more than apparent and indicated no more than the distinctive features of each separate group. It is therefore not surprising that Cuvier emphasized the search for differences and not the study of resemblances:

> To establish resemblances and to determine differences are one and the same operation and this operation constitutes the whole of descriptive natural history. To believe that certain men have devoted themselves [to the study of] differences, to reproach them for this, is an idea without foundation. It is precisely by the means of differences that resemblances are determined, since resemblances are only what remains after the differences have been removed.[23]

Cuvier's disclaimer that differences and resemblances were really the same is not altogether convincing. It is true that the former he regarded as arising from the very essence of organic nature while the latter were somewhat fortuitous combinations which remained after differences had been identified. The study of differences was thus an unavoidable consequence of the *type* concept. Resemblances other than those between closely related forms were not emphasized in this system and basic resemblances between members of different *types* were considered to be nonexistent.

Rejection of the transmutation hypothesis

Narrowly limited variation and the obvious inaccuracies of the presumed ordinal and temporal *séries* were in perfect harmony with the teachings of the *type* concept. These several reasons all concurred toward irrefutably supporting Cuvier's conclusion that there had been no transmutations of biological species. Several pages could be devoted to citing his condemnations of this idea. The substance of them all is much the same and it is sufficient to repeat here only one of his most vigorous and concise declarations.

> Without doubt, by transporting one's imagination into time and space, of which none have ever had any positive ideas, one can draw from vague and arbitrary premises conclusions of precisely the same character but, apart from these unfounded generalities, to speak clearly and with reference to the species, [to say that] this animal of the modern world descends in a direct line from this antediluvian animal, and to prove it by facts or by legitimate inductions, is what it is necessary to

do and, in the present state of knowledge, no one would even dare to attempt it.[24]

This was clearly a not uncalculated *bon mot*, for in Cuvier's opinion far too many naturalists had already dared to attempt a demonstration of the transmutation hypothesis. The pretensions of men such as De Maillet, Robinet, Rodig, and others Cuvier regarded as only minor offences to good sense. He knew that the real villain was Lamarck. Lamarck had denied the real existence of species in nature and had proposed a variant scheme of the zoological *série*. He had attempted to demonstrate the modifying influence of the environment. Worst of all, perhaps, Lamarck had refused to believe that species could become extinct. The indisputable disappearance of certain kinds of organisms which Cuvier believed had been destroyed was accounted for by Lamarck by the proposal that each had been transformed into a new and higher species.[25]

Lamarck's mechanism for the transformation of species Cuvier found especially distasteful. Lamarck had suggested that psychologically founded needs or individual efforts (*besoins*) might give rise to new organs and, by accumulation of changes, to new organisms. He continued:

Now, if new circumstances have become permanent for a race of animals [and] have given these animals new *habitudes*, that is, have evoked in them new actions which have become habitual, there will result the use of this particular part in preference to that of another and, in certain cases, the complete lack of use of such a now worthless part.[26]

At this point Cuvier's patience was exhausted. The very suggestion that *habitudes*, however they might be defined, could produce new organs and initiate the transmutation of a species struck him as perfectly absurd. "A system founded on a similar basis," he proposed, "might amuse the imagination of a poet; a metaphysician might derive from it a wholly new generation of systems; but it cannot for a moment hold the attention of anyone who has dissected a hand, a visceral organ, or even a feather." [27] *Habitudes* were absolutely unable to bring forth the necessary simultaneous alterations of all of the parts and the resulting complex organ interrelations of the healthy living body. It was "ridiculous" to suppose that the body of a quadruped, reduced to a "simple mass of paste or clay which can be molded between the fingers," can, by frequently squeezing through narrow openings, become a serpent, or that a fish, escaping from the water, will see its scales dry and then crack and thus become a feathered bird.[28] Moreover, the whole conception was nothing but a foolish circular argument. Undefined and abstract "habitual" properties (the psychological urge to fly or to swim) could only be logically concurrent with and not prior to the organs which were required to lift the bird in the air or propel the fish in the sea (IFFC 65, f. 123). Furthermore, environmental changes could not appear instantaneously. Lamarck's scheme required long periods of time. Cuvier sourly answered this claim by recalling that "time is always one of the necessary factors of all things" and therefore has no special significance for any one thing, particularly for the transmutation of species.[29]

Cuvier had already disposed of the *série*, whether proposed by Lamarck or by others. With the downfall of the scheme of environmental influences, the various kinds of animals could again be referred to clearly defined morphological *types*, the species and other groups of the zoological taxonomic system. And extinction, of course, was shown to be real, not apparent. Lamarck, Cuvier was confident, not only had failed to demonstrate any significant variability of the species but had also been completely unsuccessful in creating a mechanism which, even if the species were highly variable, might lead them along the path to transmutation.

Cuvier replaced Lamarck's view of a mutable organic creation with a straightforward and simple proposition which had long been favored by conservative and unspeculative naturalists, particularly by Linnaeus. In the beginning, Cuvier believed, God had created a pair of animals of each kind and these original couples had engendered by direct descent the entire subsequent population of the globe. Unlike Linnaeus, he recognized that there were interruptions in these series of species. Some species, he knew, had become extinct. Each species had been created by divine will and each was assigned from the beginning its special place in the economy of nature from which it could not depart. The fish, for example, were designed to move, reproduce, and die in an aqueous environment: "This is their place in the creation. They will remain there until the destruction of the present order of things." [30] Any disturbance of the relative role which each species played in the world led to a general disequilibrium, a circumstance which the balance of the forces of nature constantly tended to overcome (IFFC 94, f. 341). The stability of the separate species was paralleled by an over-all stability of the entire organic world.

Cuvier acknowledged that the center of this equilibrium was frequently changing and that this situation gave rise among the animal population to unequal opportunities for a continued healthy existence. Competition between the different organisms therefore resulted (IFFC 96, *1e leçon*):

[The] harmony and coordination of the different creatures for the general maintenance of the surface of the globe: [This is a] maintenance definitely fixed and determined, although resulting from a number of forces infinitely greater than that of the great astronomical universe. [There is an] abundance of species in each place determined by the available food. If a species becomes too abundant it attracts its enemies. It must be admitted that there is something cruel in part of these means; nature at least needs to hide it. [From this results the] prompt disappearance of the cadavers of plants and animals. [That is] why the surface of the globe is always alive and beautiful, even in the places unhealthy for man.

It is apparent that Cuvier's notion of "competition" was anything but the idea later associated with the principle of natural selection. Like the action of geological catastrophes, Cuvier's competition could eliminate certain creatures but it could not create them. It was more a salubrious world-wide sanitary mechanism than a natural force leading to the emergence of new zoological forms. This attitude toward the possible transmutational effect of competition between animals was not an uncommon one in the early nineteenth century; it was shared with Cuvier, for example, by Charles Lyell.[31]

The bulk of Cuvier's argumentation, it has been seen, was negative. He flatly opposed the idea of the temporal and ordinal *séries*, the doctrine of the morphological unity of the animal kingdom, and the suggestions that the physical environment or the competitive situation of the organic world were possibly causal factors in the transmutation of species. This argumentation was well in accord with the general Cuvierian attitude that a rout of the opposition meant the victory, and hence the justification, of one's own views. Cuvier's energies were thereby occasionally directed toward prolonged and intricate analyses and denunciations of what he regarded as pernicious zoological philosophy. He was not above attempting to exhaust a subject which had already, for all practical purposes, perished. Such, certainly, was the case with the doctrine of "organic crystallization."

Cuvier knew that the presumed spontaneous generation of individuals or species was a valueless alternative to the origin of the forms by means of a unique creative act (see Chapter II). Too patently materialistic, the former doctrine reduced the origin of complex organisms to an almost random association of brute matter or, at best, to an aggregation of particles directed by some occult, intangible force. Cuvier was especially vexed by the particular form of the argument known to him under the name "organic crystallization." According to this doctrine, which appears to have received a powerful restatement from the botanist Joseph Pitton de Tournefort early in the eighteenth century and which then continued to dominate discussion of the subject during the next several decades, there was a close analogy, if not identity, between the generation of organized creatures and the formation of mineral crystals. The latter were actually considered by many to be "living" also. The idea passed through the hands (usually with change) of innumerable philosophers, naturalists, and mineralogists, among them Maupertuis, Buffon, Bourguet, and La Mettrie. Before the end of the century, however, some professional mineralogists had rejected the parallel and had attempted to separate definitively the three so-called kingdoms of nature.[32] Thus, by the time Cuvier entered the argument in the early years of the following century, the idea was already discredited and this perhaps explains why Cuvier's criticisms exist only in manuscript lecture notes. Lamarck, it should be noted, was an exception to the rule and continued (in *Hydrogéologie* [1802] and elsewhere) to support the older viewpoint.

For Cuvier the desired refutation was astonishingly simple. A merely cursory comparison between the two modes of supposed crystallization betrayed how different they actually were. Mineral crystals were made of similar particles, situated differently, and growing by external accretion; organic "crystals," on the contrary, were built of heterogeneous units, in fixed positions, and growing by internal *augmentation*. Life, Cuvier believed, could not have arisen from the aggregation of material particles. The validity of the idea was further vitiated by the numerous purely hypothetical forces which were supposed to give it direction. Neither Buffon's *moule intérieure* nor Blumenbach's *nisus formativus* could explain or confirm the analogy (IFFC 54, f. 251). Buffon's modification of the argument, which, by introducing organic molecules, allowed him to avoid the immediate perils of spontaneous generation, was equally unsatisfactory.[33] It is therefore no surprise that the nonoccurrence of spontaneous generation, a necessary conclusion in Cuvier's general system of nature, contributed more evidence to the "fact" of the direct creation of organized animals.

Cuvier believed that the essential act of generation was the bringing forth of a preformed individual contained within the female body. The phrase "life from life," which he often repeated, meant nothing else to him than the successive emergence from generation to generation of already existing creatures. For the opening discourse to a lecture series on the phenomena and problems of animal generation, he prepared this brief resumé of the issue (1817; IFFC 106, *1ᵉ leçon*):

Generation, or the bringing forth of another organized creature capable of living . . . The germ preexists in the female prior to all copulation; proofs: animals without males, animals fecund over several generations [without additional copulation] . . . Generation therefore is and can only be the awakening of the germ. Every germ clings first of all to an individual of its own species.

Cuvier never ventured further than this simple statement. He felt that the generation of living organisms was the "most incomprehensible mystery" to be found in natural history and that of the systems advanced for its explanation the notion of the "preexistence of the *germes* was the most reassuring for the imagination."[34]

Whether the *germe* represented the actual body of the forthcoming offspring or whether it in some manner designated in general terms an undifferentiated developmental potential was left undecided. In the few cases where evidence seemed to be available — the birds, fish, and the frog — the embryo had always been discovered "formed" at the earliest possible moment of observation. The preformation of the embryo furthermore was necessary because of the "reciprocal communications" which controlled the physiological processes of the mature animal. It was impossible for Cuvier to believe that an animal could continue to exist at any stage of its life history, even the earliest, if the conditions for its functional integrity were not constantly maintained. Successive development of the various parts would produce only physiological chaos and the death of the individual. "Up to the present," he concluded, "life has always arisen from life. We see it being transmitted and never being produced, and although the impossibility of spontaneous generation may never be demonstrated absolutely, all of the efforts of physiologists who believe this sort of generation possible have not yet succeeded in presenting us with a single example of it."[35]

The system of epigenetic development was, he believed, so subject to criticism that its attacks upon the doctrine of preformation were wholly without value. To the charge that preformation left unexplained the germinal nucleus (*noeud*), he replied that the epigeneticists relied upon an equally uncertain developmental force (*moule*). Furthermore, Cuvier remarked, there was no more likelihood that organic crystallization could occur within the body than without, a statement which reveals how closely he identified the epigenetic system and the doctrine of spontaneous generation (IFFC 110, ff. 33, 33b). Without epigenetic development there was no possibility of the repetition of structural patterns from one zoological group to another. The notion of a *répétition* of parts was another of the suggestive ideas stemming from the imaginative minds of the German *Naturphilosophen*. It had a close kinship with the presumed unity of the animal kingdom since, if unity of adult forms was not altogether feasible, another brand of (developmental) unity could be found in the similarities momentarily shown in the formation of the different creatures, particularly the vertebrates.[36] Cuvier, unfortunately, was in no way an embryologist. His antidevelopmental bias told him that the repetition idea was no better than any of the other notions coming from this source. It made no difference to him that his respected colleagues Geoffroy and Marcel de Serres were eloquent proponents of a primitive form of the later recapitulation argument. The presumed repetition of parts, in no matter what order, was, he was certain, merely another zoological fallacy, composed more in fancy than in fact, and stated in "figurative language where logic cannot penetrate."[37] If there was any resemblance at all between embryos it was because they were generated by parents belonging to the same *type* and therefore already similar. Embryos of different *types* necessarily differed as did their parents. In the embryo as in the adult form (which latter Cuvier regarded as the real subject of zoology), tempero-genetic relationships were apparent only. They represented the present reality and not the historical development of different kinds of animals.

Man's place in nature

Man's place in nature posed several problems for the transformist (and antitransformist). It was first of all necessary to ask whether man, being presumably the "highest" of all animals, was also the most morphologically typical animal. It was furthermore still unclear whether all the known races of man arose from the same source or whether each race was in some way distinct and reproductively isolated. Finally, the existence or nonexistence of fossil human remains needed to be established.

Cuvier believed that man was a being qualitatively different from other animals. Early in his career he was briefly tempted to consider man the most "perfect" animal in the creation, a being at the summit of the scale of perfection, and therefore a model for the others. The presentation of the *Tableau élémentaire* was centered upon the lengthy first chapter, devoted exclusively to man. With increasing knowledge and the introduction of the four distinct *embranchements,* Cuvier realized that practical zoology could not be based entirely upon an exhaustive understanding of human structure. Man still remained the most interesting animal because we ourselves belonged to this species, and the study of man and his behavior could still "form the object of comparison" for other animals.[38] Man was of course structurally most similar to the monkey. He was composed of the same elements and the "same essential forms" as the simians and only in the relative size of various cerebral parts was the difference between the two strikingly different.[39] Naturally, this discussion was confined to the physical and mental characteristics of man; his presumed spiritual qualities were not here in question.

There were, Cuvier believed, three races of mankind: Caucasian, Mongolian, and Ethiopian (Negro). Each of these races could be subdivided into several subgroups on geographical, linguistic, and physical grounds. Remaining outside of these subdivisions were the Malay peoples, the Eskimos, and the American Indians. One character was common to all of these races, tribes, or whatever they might be called. All were interfertile and therefore, on the basis of Cuvier's definition of the species as a distinct reproductive unit, all mankind must belong to the same species.[40] Between the three primary human races there were pronounced physical differences, of which pigmentation was of only minor importance. Nose and lip size, texture of the hair, conformation of facial bones, and shape of the head and lower jaw were all factors which permitted a more scientific identification of the black, yellow, and white races.[41] Cuvier rarely engaged in discussions of the relative intelligence and hence the degree of civilization and "humanity" attained or attainable by the various races. His sentiments, however, were clear. The European, the Caucasian race, by its monuments, traditions, and religion plainly showed its superiority over the other races. Relative lack of intelligence, or "animality," was Cuvier's criterion for placing the Mongolian and Ethiopian peoples apart from and below the Caucasian nations. In a lecture series (1805–1806) on man, the quadrumanes, and the quadrupeds, he declared (IFFC 96, *31ᵉ leçon*):

> The difference between individuals is even more marked between races. It is not for nothing that the Caucasian race has gained dominion over the world and made the most rapid progress in the sciences, while the Negroes are still sunken in slavery and the pleasures of the senses and the Chinese [are lost] in the [obscurities] of a monosyllabic and hieroglyphic language. The shape of their head relates them somewhat more than us to the animals.

It would be unjust to conclude from these words that Cuvier had joined the extreme school of white supremacy. He believed that Negroes, Chinese, and members of any other race were rational and sensitive creatures and that they therefore had as much right as the white to the title of man. Slavery was degrading for both slave and master and must be abolished.[42] Whatever might be the present or past level of relative culture of the many races of mankind, all belonged to the same species, *Homo sapiens*, and all deserved to enjoy the dignity and responsibility which were representative of man. The white man's advantage was both obvious and great but it was not to be abused. A beneficent but haughty paternalism characterizes Cuvier's attitude on this subject.

The origin of the human species was no less a mystery than that of the other animals. Our only certainty was that the evidence available, admittedly slight, could not provide mankind with any great antiquity. Cuvier adopted Buckland's division of recent geological deposits into *alluvium*, loose strata containing the remains of modern or closely related species, and *diluvium*, a vast deposit, sometimes consolidated, containing bones of many unknown animals. The most singular fact about these two deposits — one quite recent and the other not too remote, being composed of the debris left by the last revolution — was the total absence of human fossils and the bones of quadrumanes. "What is astonishing," said Cuvier, "is that among all these animals, the majority of which have today their congeners in warm climates, there is not a single quadrumane; there has not been collected a single bone or tooth of a monkey, not even from extinct species of monkeys. And, of course, there are none from man." [43] Cuvier had the good fortune to be correct regarding the absence of fossil monkeys. Only in 1837, five years after his death, was the first fossil simian (*Pliopithecus*) discovered by Edouard Lartet in northern France. Cuvier appears also to have been correct with regard to human fossils. Indubitable human remains and artifacts had been discovered and Cuvier himself devoted great attention to their study. Nevertheless, in every case which he examined, from Scheuzer's *Homo testis diluvii* to Ami Boué's discoveries in the Rhine valley marls, and especially in the important finds made by Tournal and Christol after 1827 in the caves of the French Midi, he was able to demonstrate the uncertainty which persisted regarding their stratal position. Without a precise idea of the location of these fossils in the geological strata there could be no possibility of establishing their antiquity. [44] The evidence therefore proved that the human species did not exist in the same regions and at the same time as did the great species of quadrupeds recently become the object of intensive paleontological study, since man no less than these animals should be subject to fossilization.

Cuvier did not draw the expected conclusion from these discoveries. He not only did not deny the antediluvian existence of mankind but actually seemed to favor this idea. Man might have occupied small areas from which, after the passing of the revolution, he could go forth to repopulate the newly formed continents. His previous homeland might have been destroyed and submerged by the great sea of the revolution and thus his fossil remains placed wholly out of reach of modern man.[45] These ideas were in complete agreement with his conviction that migrations and not new creation(s) were responsible for the temporally different faunas of the earth.

Cuvier was perhaps one of the most famous exponents of the monogenetic origin of mankind, a viewpoint long entrenched in the Judeo-Christian tradition.[46] The idea popularized by Linnaeus and accepted by Cuvier, that each present species represents the current aggregate of individuals descended from an original conspecific pair, when associated with the denial of the transformation of species, necessitated a unitary view of the human species. The races of mankind were significant variants, to be sure, and they probably had long been distinct. Their differences, however, were acquired so long ago that it now appeared impossible to explain them. Cuvier was reduced to the amusing but not illuminating suggestion that the three major races escaped in different directions after the last revolution, some 5000 years ago, and have since had no contact with one another (IFFC 97, § II).

Perhaps the most that could be said regarding physical man, that is, man with his spiritual qualities momentarily set aside, was that no evidence of his origin could be discovered. Neither great antiquity nor recent appearance was implied; this question necessarily remained unresolved. Cuvier had furthermore given neither confirmation nor denial to the possible existence of fossil man. Just as the mummified Egyptian animals were similar to modern forms, so were the Egyptians themselves and other ancient peoples similar to modern European man. The numerous races of mankind composed, in Cuvier's opinion, a great conspecific group, each varying in appearance and relative intelligence, but all sufficiently similar in important features so as not to have departed significantly from the human *type*. Modern man was literally the same as ancient man; mankind had not evolved.

Recapitulation

Examination of the substance of Cuvier's opposition to the notion of the transmutation of species reveals that his attacks were concentrated against a set of ideas best summarized in the doctrines of Lamarck. Of these, two conceptions were regarded as particularly deleterious to the development of sound zoology. The zoological *série*, no matter how it might be stated, and speculation upon spontaneous generation were Cuvier's true *bêtes noires*. His beliefs furthermore show that it was still possible and even legitimate to avoid a definite commitment on questions, for example, man's place in nature and the meaning of vestigial organs, which would later so disturb evolutionist and antievolutionist alike. He supported his own view — the fixity of species — by pointing to the seemingly restricted variations of organized creatures and to their consequent existence as stable morphological units. Transformism was, at best, a merely possible hypothesis, and not a necessary or even a probable one.

But this is only a partial conclusion. It indicates how Cuvier dealt with zoological propositions which possessed distinct evolutionary implications and it suggests that his antitransformist viewpoint was conditioned or determined by the anatomical correlation principle. It is necessary to examine more closely Cuvier's use of this principle. In evaluating Cuvier's apology for his zoological practices one recognizes how easily and inevitably the antitransformist arguments arose from his general philosophy of nature.

VII

Cuvier and Evolution

Order is the selection of one set of appearances rather than another because it gives a better sense of the reality behind the appearances. Science is an orderly language for describing some events and predicting others like them. The order is a selection of appearances. And any selection itself implies, and imposes, an interpretation.
— J. BRONOWSKI [1]

CUVIER now stands revealed as the defender of the integrity of the individual animal and of the species and as the eloquent advocate of a wholesale return to the principles of teleological zoology. Of species transmutation he could speak only in negative terms. These zoological arguments were one motive and, it appears, by far the most important motive lying behind his rejection of the transformist doctrine. There existed a second possible motive for his opposition. Many naturalists were strongly influenced by the seeming necessity of finding in nature the literal realization of the events catalogued in Divine Scripture. On many issues of natural history, and particularly that of the nature of biological species, it was commonly believed that the Bible was to be either the final authority or at least a repository of general truths of which none could be safely or legitimately disregarded by a truly philosophical naturalist. Cuvier was fully aware of these views and, as a good Christian, he was not entirely unsympathetic toward them. He was not, however, a doctrinaire Biblical zoologist. As a basis for intelligent discussion of the problems of natural history he preferred nature and the animals to ancient nonzoological authority. Cuvier saw presented in Scripture instructions for increasing the happiness and moral well-being of mankind and not texts for the exact study of natural history; this study was the province of science and not of theology.

The correlation principle excludes species transmutation

Reduced to its simplest terms, Cuvier's zoological system was based upon a philosophy of stability. Immutability was the essence of his doctrine. Transformism demanded the major transformation of the biological species during both the present period and the extensive past history of the earth. It was to this consequence of the transformist doctrine that Cuvier most vigorously objected. Application of the principle of the correlation of parts to the over-all pattern of the animal kingdom had convinced him that the various zoological groups were the result of a harmonious assemblage of the constituent parts of each organism. The principle was, in this sense, a direct statement determining inevitably the structures of each creature. The principle was also a powerful negative tool which disclosed with equal facility which structural combinations were impossible or, in Cuvier's terms, "incompatible." "The truth remains [evident]," he declared, even

. . . after so much writing and discourse, just as we established it in an article thirty-two years ago [Introduction, *Leçons d'anatomie comparée*, edition 1] and therefore before all of these so-called philosophical excursions: Nature, inexhaustible in fecundity and omnipotent in its works, if this does not imply a contradiction, has been settled [*arretée*] in the innumerable combinations of organic forms and functions which compose the animal kingdom by physiological incompatibilities alone. It has realized all those combinations which are not repugnant [*in-*

coherent] and it is these repugnancies, these incompatibilities, this impossibility of the coexistence of one modification with another which establish between the diverse groups of organisms those separations, those gaps, which mark their necessary limits and which create the natural *embranchements*, classes, orders, and families.[2]

The gaps between species as well as these groups themselves were the direct and necessary consequence of the principle of the correlation of parts. The organism, being a functionally integrated whole each part of which stood in close relation to every other part, could not, under pain of almost immediate extinction, depart significantly from the norms established for the species by the first anatomical rule. Just as it would be a geometrical contradiction for the three angles of a triangle to exceed 180°, so it would be a physiological contradiction for a bird whose length is increased 4 times to be suspended in air by wings extended only 4 times. The correct factor would be 8 times because of the additional volume and weight. The ruminant could not have a short, straight digestive tube; the eagle was forbidden webbed feet; the serpent had no external limbs; the cave-dwelling crustacean lacked acute eyesight. The correlation of parts dictated that, in sum, any combination of organs was possible which was not in itself contradictory and that all incompatible combinations remained unrealized.[3] Cuvier's principle almost seemed to say that whatever can exist does exist, and that whatever does not exist cannot exist.

Zoologists today also believe in a correlation of parts, without which an organism would literally disintegrate, and yet they believe in evolution too. Obviously, the modern view and Cuvier's principle are not the same. What, then, is peculiar to Cuvier's correlation principle which excludes the possibility of transmutation of species?

The answer again lies in the limitation of variation by the correlation principle. It is the degree of permitted variation which now becomes crucial. Cuvier freely admitted almost unlimited intraspecific variation. The surest proof of this is the fact that he believed that no two members of a given species were morphologically alike. The correlation principle was therefore not so rigid as to prevent variation altogether. Cuvier was careful, however, to insist that variation could not extend beyond well-demarcated limits, limits which coincided with those of the species.

These small intraspecific variations were considered to be of minor zoological importance. They affected only parts of unimportant peripheral and superficial organs. There was no question about the stability of the essential organs, of the nervous system, heart, lungs, and viscera. Here one observes the two apparent levels of variation which concerned Cuvier. Intraspecific variation was structurally insignificant and aimless in direction. It also seemed to have no basic effect on the functional integrity of the organism. In contrast, variation of gross structure, of the major organs, if it occurred, would have had disastrous consequences. A major change, for example, a sharp increase in the heart beat or the diminution by half of the kidney and thus a reduction in renal secretion, would by itself have wrought havoc with the general constitution of the animal. In order that an animal might persist after a change of this magnitude it would be necessary that the other organs of the body be also proportionately modified. In other words, an organism must change en bloc or not at all. Only saltatory modification could occur, and this idea was to Cuvier, as it is to most modern zoologists, but for very different reasons, unverified and basically absurd. Transmutation by the accumulation of alterations, great or small, would thus be impossible. This would be especially true if no adequate mechanism were available to "direct" the accumulative process.

The correlation principle, as understood by Cuvier, so restricted variation as to make it "evolutionarily" insignificant. To ridicule macromutational trends was an easy task. Consequently, the principle of the correlation of parts was an elegant means of stating and demonstrating the impossibility of significant variation, that is, variation providing the basic material for the subsequent transmutation of species. Cuvier's efforts to limit the amplitude of species (and individual) variability, even under severe environmental stress, were, in the final analysis, promoted by his desire to reduce the presumed potential raw material for transmutation.

The impracticality of reproductive isolation as a readily verifiable species criterion reinforced this conclusion by compelling Cuvier the systematist to enunciate definite and unvarying structural characteristics for each species. Other taxonomic units were defined in the same manner. The species was thereby morphologically "defined," and the principle of the correlation of parts was called in to "explain" the definition. To create a sound taxonomic representation of the animal kingdom, Cuvier required more or less invariable criteria. Cuvier is perhaps the most distinguished figure in a long succession of naturalists after Linnaeus who insisted that only a clearly defined, morphologically similar group of individuals was taxonomically real, and who failed to recognize that a dynamic, variable population could also be classified.[4]

Cuvier moreover seems to have been constitutionally unable to support or to appreciate the basic idea of change. This introduces a possible third factor into the question of motives or predispositions against the transformist viewpoint. Was Cuvier's opposition determined wholly or in part by ingrained traits of character, by long-entrenched and unshakable patterns of thought? Was it really a phenomenon on the psychological level? The answer must of course be affirmative, but such a response has really little obvious additional usefulness. It explains too much, for no one would deny that the design argument of the more eager natural theologians or even Cuvier's own correlation principle were not in part and perhaps to a very great degree conditioned by their advocates' over-all intellectual attitudes. This can be illustrated by the fact that the bold thoughts of Cuvier's colleagues, Lamarck and Geoffroy, were so totally repugnant to his whole manner of thinking that it was only by great effort that he was able to form a tolerably clear idea of what these naturalists were attempting to create. His counter-argumentation, when it came, was a purely scientific affair. The ever-present psychological predispositions, if they had any major influence upon Cuvier's scientific studies, were expressed not in general and indistinct terms but always within the context of the relevant zoological issue. Cuvier's unadventurous and authoritarian spirit was unreceptive to new ideas and reluctant to alter old and accepted views. His range of vision was great, embracing all of the sciences, but his sphere of active thought was confined and was not further cultivated. He was always the legislator or universal mind, extraordinarily well informed, industrious, lucid in thought and exposition — anything, indeed, but an innovator.

If it is true that in forming a scientific system (a task which occupied Cuvier as it did his contemporaries) each researcher is compelled to select between numerous possible hypotheses to explain given phenomena, then it may be concluded that the very nature of Cuvier's intellect had already seriously reduced the number of alternatives available. Cuvier failed even to see the problem posed by the occurrence of vestigial organs. He was unable to consider seriously the possibility that the recognized sequence of fossil vertebrate animals might tell something more about the earth's history than the mere fact of organic extinction. Many other individuals, of course, suffer parallel limitations. Lamarck, for example, was so obsessed by transmutation that he denied the demonstrable occurrence of extinction. Cuvier's limited vision, however, joined to his deliberate rejection or reinterpretation of evidence favoring species transmutations, reemphasizes the absence from his zoological investigations of proper consideration for the possibility and problems of organic change.

Specific change and the Cuvierian zoological *type* were contradictory concepts. Cuvier the taxonomist demanded precise definition and long-term stability, classificatory criteria which the current transformist schemes could not provide. He found factual evidence in his zoological observations which convinced him that the biological species were unvarying and he supported his practical discoveries with physiological generalizations taken ultimately from Aristotle. The historian faces in Cuvier that extraordinary situation in which a man discovers and interprets after his own opinions data which will soon undermine his entire system. Comparative anatomy, for example, and, to a lesser extent, paleontology were among the principal disciplines which ultimately provided the factual foundations for the theory of evolution (see below). Cuvier's conservative scientific temperament helped determine which phenomena were to be regarded as valid facts and which facts were to be considered as significant, and not one of the vast store of the then available zoological data was believed to support the idea of species transmutation.[5] Demonstration of such transmutation Cuvier knew would have struck at the heart of his system and the labor and thought concentrated in the principle of the correlation of parts would have then served no end. With consistency and genuine conviction of the validity of his own system, he opposed with zoological arguments the new and disruptive doctrines. There was no other alternative before him.

The religious motive a secondary factor

The Bible was not, in Cuvier's opinion, a scientific text. Cuvier's conception of Christianity and of the teachings of the Bible stressed unquestioning faith and correct conduct and did not seek in Scripture an authoritative description of the past history and present processes of the physical world. The long and tendentious struggle between science and religion was a subject which failed entirely to please him. Religion, being essentially a question of the relation between the individual and his Creator, he regarded as unsuited for acrimonious public dispute (see Chapter I). Cuvier was so confident in his own religious convictions that he had no need to seek their confirmation in external, scientific discoveries.[6] He was aware, furthermore, that theology, like any other discipline, could be damaged by indiscriminate meddling in affairs not wholly relevant to its purposes.

A classic problem in Protestant theology had long been the relative conceptual merits regarding the existing world of nature (or reason) and divine Scripture. In Cuvier's own and other Protestant churches a crisis had been reached by the end of the seventeenth century. Luther had been especially concerned not to identify God with nature or to remove Him from effective control of His creation. God was wholly apart from the world, but still everywhere and at all times omnipotent. The successes of the Counter Reformation and the hardening of a new Lutheran scholasticism which met Roman traditionalism with Scriptural inerrancy and the elevation of Aristotle to philosophical primacy forced Protestant thought into narrow literalistic interpretations of Biblical texts. At the same time science and geographical discovery were demonstrating in a vital, tangible manner the existence and fascination of the physical world. There came to certain of the pious the idea of seeking God not in the historical, ecclesiastical context but in nature. God to these believers became above all a Creator God.[7] The stage was now set for the prolonged battle throughout the eighteenth and nineteenth centuries, within and without the churches and fought by believers, deists, and atheists, over the various means of demonstrating God's existence and His attributes. Science, especially biology and geology, became, for better or worse, one of the principal armaments of Christian apologetics.

Those whose faith was secure might nevertheless be bothered by possible consequences of Christian doctrine for scientific belief, or vice versa. Certainly the questions of the origin and nature of man, of the creation of the world and of living things, and the scientific meaning or explanation of the Noachian Deluge were issues with which any sensitive or literalistically inclined Christian thinker would have to deal. Cuvier, it has been seen, considered the scientific evidence bearing on each of these issues. He found no evidence for the great antiquity of man, but also did not demand recent human origins. The nature of man was a psychophilosophical or even a religious problem; zoology could only discuss man's physical state. There was, furthermore, no scientific evidence telling of the presumed creation of the world or of life on the earth. Creation was a mystery still untouched by science. Memories of a great Deluge were known to exist in the records of ancient societies. It was already clear, however, that this Deluge had not caused all mankind to perish and Cuvier was careful to admit the possibility that antediluvian man had existed.

Cuvier was concerned with demonstrating the noncontradiction between science and religion. He was not seeking a positive concordance between them. He believed that the spirit of the sciences and that of religion could exist together. Although science provided the only uncontested truths to which man could aspire, it was no less true that the greatest natural philosophers were also deeply religious men. Newton, Leibniz, and Pascal were cited by Cuvier as examples showing that "geometers" and "physicists" may also be men devoted to Christianity (IFFC 161, ff. 6–7). This does not mean, of course, that Cuvier's popular scientific expositions, the two geological *Discours*, were devoid of religious presuppositions and implications. The tone of these treatises is clear. Throughout the *Discours* are poorly concealed attempts to show the simultaneity of the most recent catastrophe and the Noachian Deluge, to emphasize the recent appearance of civilized man, and to prove that destruction and migration, and not successive creations, were responsible for the history of life on the earth. Cuvier's treatises were strikingly different from those written by naturalists who were also natural theologians. Cuvier had great admiration for the intricacies of the parts of the organic world, but he never used these latter to demonstrate, by analogy or design, the existence and action of the Creator. Even less does one find in Cuvier's works the overt application of the results of zoology and geology to the specifically theologically conditioned interpretations of the earth's history of the kind which appeared from the hands of William Buckland or Adam Sedgwick. Here is one of the notable characteristics of Cuvier's writings: a deliberate attempt not to mix science and religion. The *Discours* are, even with their numerous errors, scientific treatises. They are not noisy, apologetic religious tracts.

An author, especially an author as familiar with the achievements of his science as Cuvier, in 1812 or even in 1830 still enjoyed the great "benefit of a doubt" conferred by unavoidable ignorance. Fossil man was yet so poorly known that he became no hindrance to a literalistic interpretation of Scripture. And Cuvier, as has been shown above, was not committed to proving a priori man's lack of antiquity. He was also secure when disallowing all appeals to investigate or to describe the creation(s). Skepticism, meaning "no grounds for discussion," on this subject was among his most valuable contributions to the investigation of earth history. Lamarck, for example, had vainly devoted innumerable pages of his wildest fancies to developing an almost completely worthless hypothesis for the origin of life. Cuvier's advocacy of geological catastrophism was perhaps his greatest violation of contemporary scientific knowledge. Here he confined his attention to a limited and special geological system. He was unable to escape his early studies of Wernerian geology and was, ironically, perhaps somewhat influenced by the prevailing mood of great and forceful change which was current in a revolutionary age. Cuvier was therefore able to accept, on the grounds of noncontradiction, both a not too literal reading of the Mosaic narrative and the results of modern science. Areas of conflict were still ill-defined and some sciences, particularly historical zoology, were still in a rude state.

Perhaps Cuvier saw that the real danger of science for religion was not in specific problems such as the nature and date of the Deluge or the origin of man. On all of these points Cuvier and a growing number of his contemporaries were content to use the Mosaic texts as a definitive source only for the period following the Noachian Deluge and the subsequent resurgence of humanity at this time, that is, the formation and perpetuation after this disastrous event of civilized societies with oral or written records.[8] When, in passing comment, Cuvier criticized Descartes and the *Philosophes*, praised Newton and Aristotle, and attacked the *Idéologues* and the *Naturphilosophen*, he was not always guided by purely scientific considerations. Cartesianism and the Enlightenment philosophy were dangerous because they had not confined their critical enquiry to proper limits and, while criticism was useful in the sciences, authority must prevail in other areas of human endeavor, including religion.[9] By emphasizing scientific methods and achievements, which would permit science to encroach upon the unique elements of the religious experience, he feared that only crass materialism could result. Materialism could only mean the illegitimate divorce of the Creator from His universe, a situation which Cuvier would not tolerate.

The *Naturphilosophen* and the emerging French philosophical school of eclecticism, centered about German philosophy, were guilty of another crime. This was pantheism, wherein God and His universe and all spiritual and existing things merged to become only One. Cuvier's distaste for the *Naturphilosophen* has already been noted. There exists a transcript of his marginal notes to V. Cousin's *Fragments philosophiques*, a basic manual of eclecticism, in which he alternately shouts "pantheist" and "hypocritical piety" at Cousin's profession of faith and accuses him of dissimulating his true "Spinozism" (IFFC 316(5)). Materialism and pantheism were terms of bitterest reproach for Cuvier. Pantheism he employed more frequently, but perhaps only because this was a prevailing doctrine after the decline of Enlightenment materialism and also during his own lifetime. Both doctrines attempted to solicit support from the sciences and it was these pseudoscientific pretensions which most annoyed Cuvier, since they gave the appearance that science was not nonreligious but antireligious. God's existence and the certainty of His benevolent concern for all mankind were never questioned by Cuvier. He admitted freely that nature was a "happy allegory which plainly teaches us that one of our first duties is to fill our minds with the goodness and wisdom of the Author of

Nature by a continued study of the products of His power." [10] It should be noted that this passage, of a tone rare in Cuvier's works, mentions only the attributes of the Creator; His existence was assumed and was considered beyond question. The sciences might stimulate our religious sensibility or initiate us into the more profound riches of the Christian tradition, but they had nothing to say concerning the personal faith of the believer.

A further word is necessary upon the role of religious motives in Cuvier's thought. To argue that his religious convictions were not directly involved in the refutation of the transformist doctrine does not entirely remove them from the historian's attention. It was perfectly obvious, although unstated, that the principle of the correlation of parts was understood by the naturalist to have been decreed by God Himself. The correlation principle was the prime example in natural history of the presumed fundamental lawfulness of nature. Hence, the question arises, is the fact that religious considerations lay behind an essentially zoological generalization an appropriate index of the possible influence of these views on Cuvier's rejection of the idea of the transmutation of species?

This question may perhaps best be answered by distinguishing between religious motives and religious arguments. The former are never absent from Cuvier's thought and no one should or can attempt to minimize their importance. As has been seen above, demonstration of the noncontradiction of science and religion was a central feature of Cuvier's task. But the use or justification of individual theological arguments in their literal form was not a part of his study. Without considerable exegesis, Genesis does not insist upon the absolute stability of biological species. Genesis tells of the creation of the original pairs of organized beings and it is understood that these are the direct predecessors of those kinds of animals and plants still living. On this point, certainly, Cuvier is in complete agreement with Scripture. It is clear, however, that he considered reproductive continuity to be also a primary biological fact, a fact made inescapable by the studies and writings of Harvey,

Linnaeus, and many others. It was not on inflexible religious dogma but on scientific authority that he based his argument. If Moses recorded the extinction of great numbers of creatures during the Deluge, he did not have in mind a series of disasters which, over a long span of centuries, destroyed various kinds of animals and plants. Cuvier adopted a system of geobiological catastrophes, and this without hesitation or with any concern that these events were unrecorded in Scripture.

It would be interesting to know how Cuvier would have reacted had it not been possible that scientific belief and religious dogma might then still exist in reasonably harmonious accord. As to all historical questions of this kind, no answer can be given. The significant fact is that Cuvier believed, rightly or wrongly, that they were in accord. Further interrogation was considered unnecessary. It was Cuvier's peculiar conception of zoology which provided his arguments against transformism. Moses and Scripture did not speak to scientists *qua* scientists. The problem of the possible transmutation of species Cuvier regarded as a scientific affair and not a theological issue. Theology, trespassing without warrant on forbidden grounds, often had lost more than it had stood to gain.

After Cuvier and toward evolution

There have already been frequent occasions to call attention to the paradox that, whereas Cuvier himself vigorously opposed the transmutation idea, his studies in comparative anatomy and paleontology helped to prepare the climate in which the theory of organic evolution later developed. Certain elements of Cuvier's antitransformism were perhaps indispensable to the formulation of evolutionary theory. At the same time his direct spiritual disciples, naturalists and zoologists of the caliber of Louis Agassiz, Richard Owen, P. M. Flourens, and many others, were altogether too subservient to their master's philosophy to wish or to be able to break away from his intellectual dominion. The development of evolutionary ideas in the half-century prior to the *Origin of species* is an enormously complex and still inadequately explored subject. The following review attempts only to suggest the possible influence of Cuvier's ideas on this development.

Cuvier passed along to later biologists a heightened realization of the functional integrity of the individual organism. Without recognizing the significance of his own achievement, Cuvier was in great part responsible for focusing the attention of botanists and zoologists upon the problems of biological adaptation. Adaptation, the close adjustment of over-all organic structure and functions to one another and to long-term external conditions, is a phenomenon of greatest importance for evolutionary theory and is also among the phenomena which this theory has accounted for most successfully. Cuvier was able to see that the organism maintained and reproduced itself under often highly unfavorable conditions. This circumstance, according to his system, was a necessary consequence of the conditions of existence. Each kind of animal was provided by the Creator with whatever structures, behavior patterns, and so on would best maintain the individual or group in the varying organic economy of the world. The world was populated by many and different kinds of creatures, and organic diversity was one of the best-established lessons of natural history. But this diversity was not unlimited, even in theory, and herein lay the burden of Cuvier's argument. In all instances the correlation principle "explained" the occurrence of different creatures and also denied existence to any important divergences from the *type*. Applying his laws of organic correlation, he saw animal organization submitted to morphological demands expressed in the rules governing the vital processes of the organism, but he failed to recognize that these correlations, that the adaptations of the parts of the organism to one another and of the whole creature to prolonged external conditions, could be due to exclusively "natural" forces. Hindsight must be denied the critic: it was not until Darwin's clarification of the effectiveness of natural selection acting upon small variations that a plausible mechanism for the production of observed adaptations was enunciated. It has been seen that Cuvier was thoroughly dissatisfied with the one serious contemporary proposal of a "natural" adaptive mechanism and that he rejected Lamarck's suggestion of environmental influences as much for its dangerous materialistic tendencies as for its strictly scientific inadequacies. But, beyond these several qualifications, one basic fact is seen to pervade Cuvier's entire zoological system, and this is the fact of adaptive diversity itself. The *type* concept destroyed the possibility of a simplistic representation of organic nature. As Lamarck demonstrated in his later works and as all subsequent advocates of the doctrine of descent with modification understood, it was clearly impossible that all kinds of organisms had arisen serially from one or even a few primitive forms. Descent had to be sought elsewhere than in a unique zoological *série*. The recognition that organic nature was orderly yet diverse was surely one of Cuvier's greatest contributions to science, and it detracts little from his accomplishment that the order of nature is accounted for today by the operation of forces peculiar to nature herself and not by conservative rules imposed upon nature by her Creator.

Cuvier's destruction of the zoological *série* had been accompanied by the demonstration of an indisputable faunal succession. In general, the remains of structurally more complex organisms characterized the more superficial geological deposits, while deeper strata preserved the impressions of lesser creatures. This statement is essentially ambiguous and must necessarily be so. There was, in Cuvier's opinion, no single criterion or set of criteria which would permit a naturalist to assign degrees of perfection to any organism whatsoever. For Cuvier the geopaleontological sequence was merely a record of organic succession and not of organic progression, of an advancing replacement of faunas culminating, as stated by the classic progressionists, in the appearance of man. His system was based on the simple fact of faunal replacement. He deliberately avoided the temptation to place all of these creatures in a single or even a partially ramified line reaching from the simplest to the most complex organism. Progressionism was in part an ill-disguised return to the old unique *série*. The *série* this time was based more on paleontological than on taxonomic evidence. Cuvier's paleontological studies had shown, however, that the fossil record failed to support zoological progression just as morphological and taxonomic evidence had failed to support the ordinal *série* (see Chapter VI). This is an historically complex situation, for the special feature of progressionism was its denial of the possibility that the various kinds of organisms found in the fossil series really represented the historical development of life. The progressionists, and Cuvier, refused categorically to admit that the different fossil groups were genetically related to one another and to modern forms. Neither the progressionists nor Cuvier could accept descent with modification. An era of intense paleontological activity followed Cuvier's pioneering studies and there were indeed few of these paleontologists who were transmutationists. Owen and other English geologists, Agassiz, Elie de Beaumont, and Adolfe Brongniart all agreed with the main teachings of Cuvier. Flourens, Cuvier's self-appointed interpreter but no paleontologist, and A. D. d'Orbigny were the principal proponents of the successive catastrophe doctrine. D'Orbigny in 1849 had already identified at least 27 distinct geological and faunal periods and thus revealed 27 pairs of catastrophe and creation. That the known fossil record in 1830, or in 1859, could not compel naturalists to acknowledge a sequential development of even a single species or genus is seen from the fact that T. H. Huxley, in 1870, was embarrassed by the difficulty of finding a suitable example to illustrate the contribution of paleontology to evolution.[11] Nevertheless, Cuvier's successionism and the progressionist doctrine which arose from it were among the first truly scientific indications of the long and confused faunal history of the earth. Zoology and geology would henceforth work together in reconstructing this history.

From the revelations of comparative anatomy and paleontology, two sciences whose development is due more to Cuvier than to perhaps any other individual, came the surprising conclusion that the surface of the earth had in the past been inhabited by a succession of different and well-defined populations of animals. Here was a fact which accorded well with the transformist view of nature, a view which Cuvier had wholly failed to appreciate. He chose to interpret this evidence in precisely the opposite manner and his opposition to the transmutation idea can be traced to the teleological sources of the *type* concept. Cuvier's most brilliant achievement and his greatest failure are joined in the *type* concept and the philosophical principles with which it was associated. Cuvier linked the reality and the immutability of the biological species, and justified both with the principle of the correlation of parts. By applying one of the oldest of all biological generalizations, Aristotle's functional conception of the organism, Cuvier rejected the early and perhaps premature statement of another and yet still more fruitful and exciting doctrine, the idea of the transformation of species.

Appendix A

[Fragment on artificial and natural classificatory systems]

One may select various kinds of characters; actually, all those which are constant may be employed . . . This kind of character gives no general information about each group. They [produce] what are called *artificial Systems*. Their advantage is to be easy to make and to apply (if this is done according to the rules). The rules are: 1. Applicability must exist in all instances. Nothing may be excluded. Dichotomy is always the basis. It is erroneous to wish to separate this system from analysis. Both are always essentially dichotomous. 2. Nothing variable may be used as a character: neither the size, the color, or the integument of certain species, nor even the number of various parts. 3. The characters must be taken from the object itself, and not from the climate, medical and economic properties, behavior and physical properties, culture, manner of birth, or from the names which have been employed. 4. When an organism passes through various stages one must pay attention to the perfect [final] stage. It is better to create a separate system for transitory stages such as the larvae, buds, leaves, etc.

With these rules, and those of [verbal] expression which will be presented elsewhere [see Chapter III], one can make an adequate artificial system. Nevertheless, those who have made them have also done something more. In some way they have had in mind the general notion of the natural system [*méthode*]. That is why Linnaeus said *genera naturalia sunto . . .*

A natural system can in fact possess additional utility, particularly that of expressing everything in the least terms, by generalizing its terms as much as possible. This is really the definitive end, the ideal, of every system. The only way to attain this goal is to bring together in one division at no matter what level all those creatures which resemble one another more than they resemble any member of another division of the same level. The resemblance[s] must therefore become closer as the divisions become narrower or lower. This is the natural system.

The principal objection which might be made against it is that it has no sharply defined divisions. Some people have even thought that it means arranging the creatures so that there would always be a transition [*passage*] from one to another. This has been called the scale of being. Founded on the proposition of Leibniz that nature makes no leaps it related to successive events, not to simultaneously existing creatures. Actually, it does not exist. Proofs: the bat, the cetaceans, the flying fish, etc. There will be instead relationships extending in all manner of directions; the former kind [that is, serial relationships] do not always occur. Those which have been sought are for the most part illusory . . . This is true [because] all combinations are not possible and [because] there are some which are mutually exclusive.

The natural system can be prepared in two ways: 1. a posteriori, by direct observation; 2. a priori, by the principle of the subordination of characters. What this subordination is; relations of the functions with one another:

> circulation and irritability; irritability and the nervous force, these two maintained by the circulation, which is maintained by digestion, which is maintained by the nervous force and irritability.

Influence of certain functions on the others:

> movement and type of nutrition (feet and teeth),
> respiration and amount of movement (lungs and wings), both of these plus the amount of digestion (stomachs of birds and reptiles),
> amount of movement and of sensibility (birds: modification of certain senses, eye, and feathers).

The characters taken from important organs must bear only on the conditions which determine their influence.

Cuvier, Institut de France, *fonds Cuvier*, 98.

Appendix B

Essay on zoological analogies

Everything may exist which does not contain within itself the principle of contradiction. There are geometrical contradictions, in terms of 180 degrees contained within 3 angles. There are others which are less obvious and which are found only by long study: the equality of the sum of the distances from the foci of the ellipse to all points on the circumference. Similarly, there are physical contradictions: oxide more than metal in a closed vessel where there is no oxygen to make it. There are also physiological contradictions. A very large bird supports itself [in the air]: if it is made 4 times longer, its new wing surface will be increased 16 times and its weight 64 times (whose square root is 8). It would need wings 8 times longer. The organism, nourished and growing by intussusception, mobile and hence not tied to the earth, and whose fluids cannot circulate by the action of weight, heat, and evaporation, must contain within itself a reservoir of nutritional material. This is the only material condition of animality.

Among the enormous number of animals made possible by this one condition there are some which are necessarily quite similar and others which are less closely related. These relationships may be of various degrees of closeness. All combinations [of organs, functions, and so forth] which are not contradictory are possible; in other words, everything which has a "condition of existence," whose parts cooperate in a common action, is possible.

Hence there must be a series of similar creatures which reaches just to the point of this contradiction. They are similar in form, composition, and functions. Differences occur first in things of small importance, in proportions. Later on come the deficiencies and additions. Only much later does a change of plan, [an alteration] of the relationship of the parts, appear.

It is in this sense that we can say that Nature employs as much as possible the same materials and preserves the same organs. She does not elongate the legs of an ox in order to make a giraffe, nor those of a rat to make a jerboa. She does not add vertebrae to the vertebrates in order to make a serpent or an eel. These are instances of the proportional differences between analogous parts (puerility of what is said about the inverse proportions of the parts).

This is the sense in which it has been figuratively stated that, within certain limits, there is a similitude of plan and of composition. This is what has always been said and, if the new naturalists mean only this, then they are merely repeating what has always been said and known. But their expressions appear to say something which is new: unity of plan, unity of composition, development from class to class, polarization, repetition.

189

Does it result from these resemblances that there exists any of the following? 1. *Unity of plan,* insofar as it concerns the general arrangement of the parts? No. Nothing is common between a medusa and a bird. 2. *Unity or identity of composition* concerning the number of parts? No, not even from one vertebrate to another, not even for a single part (head or arm). 3. *A continuous series?* No. 4. *Development* from one class to another? No. 5. *Polarization?* No. Even if there is some resemblance between the arm and the leg there is nothing in common between head and tail. 6. *Repetition?* No, nothing in common between the diverse layers.

We have tried to discover why some men believe in the [animal and plant] series, in the indistinguishable gradations, and in the transitions [*passages*] from one form to another. We have made clear that among the innumerable organic combinations which form the various animals there are some which exhibit many similarities, Nature employing here similar means, but that even then she has not been confined to the point of always having placed the same pieces in the same directions. Indeed, far from this happening, there are very great differences even between the most obvious similar animals (the vertebrates), differences of number, arrangement, and function.

We have next established that there are interruptions in the series, gaps [*hiatus*] exist; and that one comes [ultimately] to other *embranchements,* to animals which resemble the [vertebrates] only in the common conditions of animality.

Cuvier, Institut de France, *fonds Cuvier,* 94, ff. 382–388.

Bibliography of Primary Sources

A. *Unpublished Cuvier material*

It is very unusual to find revisions on the manuscripts of Cuvier's published works and extensive corrections are almost nonexistent. Rough sketches and outlines in the preserved Cuvier papers are equally uncommon. The only significant exceptions to this rule are the lengthy additions included in later editions of his works, particularly the second editions of the *Règne animal* and the *Leçons d'anatomie comparée*. The most valuable Cuvier manuscripts are therefore the notes prepared for lecture series, for *éloges*, and for special studies, or those gathered in anticipation of later publication. The number of these notes is enormous, although by no means all of them are of equal value. Letters addressed to Cuvier are also abundant. It is probable that the Institut de France and the Muséum d'histoire naturelle possess the overwhelming majority of these pieces. Letters written by Cuvier are, unfortunately, much less readily available. Those very few which still seem to exist are scattered in libraries in Europe and America. Only one substantial, and very important, collection of his letters has been published.

Two Paris libraries contain, thanks to donations by the nephew of the naturalist, the bulk of unpublished Cuvier material: the Bibliothèque de l'Institut de France and the Bibliothèque du Muséum d'histoire naturelle. Catalogues are available for each of these collections. The catalogue of the Muséum mss. is extremely summary and provides only an initial guide to the collection: [A. Boinet], *Catalogue général des manuscrits des bibliothèques publiques de France, Paris-Tome II, Muséum d'histoire naturelle*, etc. (Paris, 1914), esp. pp. 107–113. That of the *fonds Cuvier* at the Institut, however, is annotated in detail and is invaluable: H. Dehérain, *Catalogue des manuscrits du fonds Cuvier* (Paris, 1908), two parts. See also H. Dehérain, "Les manuscrits scientifiques de Cuvier," *Journ. des savants*, new ser. (*an* 2), 190–195 [1904]. The following review attempts only to call attention to major items in these collections. The numbers represent the entries in the catalogues of the two libraries and are not page references.

The Muséum possesses the dissection and reading notes (605–614) made for the *Leçons d'anatomie comparée*, which include Cuvier's additions to an interfoliated copy of the Introduction to the first edition (606) used for the second edition. Items 617–624 are the mss. of the first eight volumes of the *Histoire naturelle des poissons*. The Muséum also possesses Cuvier's notes and correspondence (627–636), plus fragments of the ms. text (ed. 1: 631–632; ed. 2: 633), relating to the *Recherches sur les ossemens fossiles*. Items 633, 634, and, especially, 627 are extremely rich in correspondence concerning the study of fossil remains. Letters from von Schlotheim, Blumenbach, Kielmeyer, the Delucs, Wm. Clift, Lyell, Buckland, Prévost, de Serres, Murchison, and others are found here.

191

At the Institut are located the notes and mss. of the *Règne animal* (ed. 1: 1–7; ed. 2: 10), the *Tableau élémentaire* (11–13), the *Rapport historique sur les progrès des sciences naturelles depuis 1789* (139), and the many memoirs on mollusks (14–39). Other large blocks of material include notes for lectures on the history of science (89–94; volume one alone of the published edition accurately represents Cuvier's plan for this work), notes, memoirs, and drawings from the Debate of 1830 (60–68), Cuvier's natural history diaries from Stuttgart and Normandy (41–49), the very extensive materials collected for the *éloges* (143–213), and the many hundreds of letters received by Cuvier between 1788 and 1832 (215–255). Also at the Institut are notes prepared by Cuvier for several of his lecture courses (102–112). Of these, numbers 103 (a course on geology forming the basis of the *Discours sur les révolutions de la surface du globe*) and 104 (anatomical lectures leading to the formation of the four *embranchements*) are particularly noteworthy. Part Two of Dehérain's catalogue lists the many pieces relating to Cuvier's administrative and educational careers, family and civil documents, honors and diplomas, and so forth preserved by the Institut.

In the P.M. Flourens papers, again at the Institut, is found a ms. copy of Cuvier's "autobiography," written in 1823 [*Ancien et nouveau fonds* 2598(3)]. This copy of 78 pages is in the hand of Mme. Cuvier. Flourens published a truncated (ca. 60 percent of the original) and altered version of this text in his *Recueil des éloges historiques* (Paris, 1856), I, 167–193. This document does not appear in the several separate editions of Flouren's *éloge* of Cuvier. The author is presently preparing an annotated edition of this essay.

The library of the Société de l'histoire du protestantisme français conserves various documents concerning Cuvier's administration of the non-Catholic churches of France. The library of the Académie des sciences, the Bibliothèque Nationale, and the Archives Nationales contain few directly relevant unpublished items. The Universiteitsbibliotheek, Amsterdam, possesses a series of more than thirty letters on paleontological subjects addressed by Cuvier to A. G. Camper (Camper's letters are in the *fonds Cuvier* and at the Muséum). Cuvier's letters on zoological subjects to his Stuttgart friend, J. H. F. Autenrieth, are held by the Universitätsbibliothek, Tübingen. Wilhelm Keiper (Berlin) owns several late letters from Cuvier to Kielmeyer; the undoubtedly very interesting early letters could not be located. It has been similarly impossible to locate letters to the Delucs and to J. A. H. Reimarus, a friend in Hamburg from whom Cuvier received several communications.

B. *Published Cuvier material*

A complete listing of every discourse, report, scientific memoir, or volume published by Cuvier would exceed three hundred items. Many of these entries are repetitive. The *Recherches sur les ossemens fossiles* and the volume of memoirs on the mollusks, for example, are really little more than collections of previously published studies. Many elements of the *Règne animal* also were issued before this great work appeared. The several collected editions of *éloges*, annual reports, occasional addresses, and so forth similarly reprint earlier articles. Published books are therefore the principal primary source for the study of Cuvier's scientific ideas. A number of fundamental zoological articles which were not reprinted nevertheless must not be overlooked.

There are three especially useful bibliographies of Cuvier's published works —books and articles—although none of them is complete or entirely reliable. By far the best bibliography of Cuvier's scientific articles on all subjects is that compiled and published by the Royal Society of London: *Catalogue of scientific papers (1800–1863)* (London, 1868), II, 114–122. In addition to references to the original French publication of these papers, the Royal Society *Catalogue* includes citations of German and English translations and review notices of these works, and thereby provides a simple index to the extraordinary radiation of Cuvier's ideas throughout Europe. The bibliography of primary sources in H. Daudin's study, *Les classes zoologiques et l'idée de série animale* (Paris, 1926), II, 279–318, includes an excellent section on Cuvier (pp. 285–293). Daudin's accuracy far exceeds that of the Royal Society, but his list is confined primarily to anatomical and taxonomic treatises, and Cuvier's more general writings and especially his geological writings are neglected. Like the Royal Society and Daudin, G. L. Duvernoy, in his bibliography of Cuvier's works, *Notice historique sur les ouvrages et la vie de M. le Baron Cuvier* (Paris-Strasbourg, 1833), 155–172, prepared a chronological listing. The chief advantage of his list is the absence of the usual bibliographical apparatus; the reader can see at a glance the outline of Cuvier's scientific career as portrayed by articles and books selected by another distinguished naturalist.

The printed catalogue of the Bibliothèque Nationale, *Catalogue général des livres imprimés de la Bibliothèque Nationale* (Paris, 1908), XXIV, cols. 983–1000, is not as useful as one might expect since copies of early editions of several of Cuvier's works are lacking. The British Museum *Catalogue of printed books* (XLVI, cols. 727–739) serves as a guide to English editions of Cuvier's works and the Library of Congress catalogue (XXXVI, 12–15) does the same for American editions.

Perhaps the best guides to more esoteric Cuvier items, as well as to the major works, are the author and subject card file in the library of the Muséum d'histoire naturelle. The resources of this library in works on all aspects of biology are enormous and well catalogued. It is unfortunate, however, that no separate list of Cuvier's private library, a magnificent collection acquired after the naturalist's death by the State for the Muséum, is available. Cuvier's books, each with a distinctive title-page mark, are scattered in the general holdings of the library and only by a combination of divination and trial and error can they be obtained. In the United States, the card file (by author) of the Museum of Comparative Zoology (Cambridge, Massachusetts) is a convenient tool for Cuvier studies. The MCZ possesses the large

Agassiz collection of offprint copies of Cuvier's scientific articles and has a very complete representation of the various editions of his larger works.

With these aids available the following concise bibliography of Cuvier's writings makes no attempt to be exhaustive. There are included below, in two categories (articles and books; letters), all of the works cited in this book and several other items of general interest.

1. *Georges Cuvier: articles and books*

1792 "Mémoire sur les Cloportes terrestes," *Journ. d'histoire naturelle*, 2: 18–31.

1795 "Discours prononcé par le citoyen Cuvier à l'ouverture du cours d'anatomie comparée qu'il fait au Muséum national d'histoire naturelle pour le citoyen Mertrud," *Magasin encyclopédique*, 5: 145–155.

1795 "Mémoire sur la structure interne et externe, et sur les affinités des animaux auxquels on a donné le nom de Vers," *Décade philosophique*, 5: 385–396.

1795 With E. Geoffroy Saint-Hilaire, "Mémoire sur une nouvelle division des Mammifères et sur les principes qui doivent servir de base dans cette sorte de travail," *Magasin encyclopédique*, 2: 164–190.

1798 *Tableau élémentaire de l'histoire naturelle des animaux* (Paris: Baudouin), pp. 710.

1799 "Mémoire sur les espèces d'éléphans vivantes et fossiles," *Mém. de l'Institut (Class. math. phys.)*, 2: 1–22.

1800– *Leçons d'anatomie comparée* (Paris: Baudouin), 5 vols. [Vols. 1–2
1805 edited by C. Duméril, 1800, and vols. 3–5 edited by G. L. Duvernoy, 1805.]

1801 "Extrait d'un ouvrage sur les espèces de quadrupèdes dont on a trouvé les ossemens dans l'intérieur de la terre," *Journ. de physique*, 52: 253–267.

1802 "Sur les vers qui ont le sang rouge," *Bull. scientifique de la Société philomatique*, no. 64, 121–122.

1803 "Notice sur l'établissement de la collection d'anatomie comparée du Muséum," *Ann. du Muséum*, 2: 409–414.

1807 "Rapport de l'Institut national . . . sur un ouvrage de M. André, ayant pour titre: Théorie de la surface actuelle de la terre," *Journ. des mines*, 21: 413–430; also *Mém. de l'Institut (Class. math. phys.)*, 8: 128–145.

1808 With others, "Rapport fait à l'Institut sur un mémoire de MM. les docteurs Gall et Spurzheim," *Ann. du Muséum*, 11: 329–375.

1810 *Rapport historique sur les progrès des sciences naturelles depuis 1789 et sur leur état actuel* (Paris: Imprim. impériale), pp. 299.

1811 With Alex. Brongniart, *Essai sur la géographie minéralogique des environs de Paris avec une carte géognostique et des coupes de terrain* (Paris: Baudouin), pp. 280.

BIBLIOGRAPHY

1812   "Animal," *Dictionnaire des sciences médicales* (Paris: Panckouke), II, 142–145.

1812   *Recherches sur les ossemens fossiles de quadrupèdes* (Paris: Déterville), 4 vols.

1812   "Sur la composition de la tête osseuse dans les animaux vertébrés," *Ann. du Muséum*, *19*: 123–128.

1812   "Sur un nouveau rapprochement à établir entre les classes qui composent le règne animal," *Ann. du Muséum*, *19*: 73–84.

1816   "Animal," *Dictionnaire des sciences naturelles* (Strasbourg-Paris: Levrault), II, 158–174.

1816   "Prospectus," *Dictionnaire des sciences naturelles* (Strasbourg-Paris: Levrault, I, v–xvi.

1817   *Mémoires pour servir à l'histoire et à l'anatomie des Mollusques* (Paris: Déterville), 23 memoirs separately paginated.

1817   *Le règne animal distribué d'après son organisation pour servir de base à l'histoire naturelle des animaux et d'introduction à l'anatomie comparée* (Paris: Déterville), 4 vols.; vols. 1, 2, and 4 by Cuvier and vol. 3 by P. A. Latreille.

1821–   *Recherches sur les ossemens fossiles* (Paris: Dufour et d'Ocagne), com-
1824   pletely revised edition.

1825   "Nature," *Dictionnaire des sciences naturelles* (Strasbourg-Paris: Levrault), XXXIV, 261–268.

1825   *Recherches sur les ossemens fossiles* (Paris: Dufour et d'Ocagne), third edition.

1828–   *Histoire des progrès des sciences naturelles de 1789 jusqu'à ce jour*
1833   (Paris: Baudouin), 5 vols.; supplementary volumes to the Baudouin *édition* of the works of Buffon.

1828–   With A. Valenciennes, *Histoire naturelle des poissons* (Paris: Levrault), 8 vols.
1833

1829   "Discours de M. le Baron Cuvier [sur le prix de Vertu]," *Recueil des*
(1843)   *discours, rapports, et pièces diverses lus dans les séances publiques et particulières de l'Académie Française, 1820–1829* (Paris: Imprim. royale), pp. 667–677.

1829   With C. Duméril, "Rapport sur un mémoire de M. Roulin, ayant pour objet la découverte d'une nouvelle espèce de Tapir dans l'Amérique du sud, fait à l'Académie royale des sciences," *Ann. des sci. naturelles*, *17*: 107–112.

1829–   *Le règne animal distribué d'après son organisation pour servir de base*
1830   *à l'histoire naturelle des animaux et d'introduction à l'anatomie comparée* (Paris: Déterville), 5 vols. Vols. 1 and 2 (1829) and 3 (1830) by Cuvier and vols. 4 and 5 (1829) by P. A. Latreille.

1830   "Considérations sur les Mollusques, et en particulier sur les Céphalopodes," *Ann. des sci. naturelles*, *19*: 241–259.

1841–   *Histoire des sciences naturelles, depuis leur origine jusqu'à nos jours,*
1845   *chez tous les peuples connus, professée au Collège de France par*

Georges Cuvier, complétée, rédigée, annotée et publiée par M. Magdeleine de Saint-Agy (Paris: Fortin, Masson), 5 vols.

1861 *Recueil des éloges historiques lus dans les séances publiques de l'Institut de France* (Paris: Firmin Didot), 3 vols.

2. *Georges Cuvier, published letters*

1833 G. Silbermann, "Lettres sur l'entomologie, par Georges Cuvier," *Rev. entomologique, 1*: 143–160.

1858 *Lettres de Georges Cuvier à C. H. Pfaff, 1788–1792, sur l'histoire naturelle, la politique, et la littérature. Traduites de l'allemand par Louis Marchant* (Paris: Masson), pp. 314.

1905 J. Viénot, "Lettres inédites de Georges Cuvier à Georges Duvernoy," *Rev. chrétienne, 52*: 42–57.

1963 W. Coleman, "A note on the early relationship between Louis Agassiz and Georges Cuvier," *Journ. history of medicine, 18*: 51–63.

C. *Published material by other authors*

André Chrysologue Gy, *Théorie de la surface de la terre, ou plutôt, recherches impartiales sur le temps et l'arrangement actuel de la surface de la terre, fondées uniquement sur les faits, sans systèmes et sans hypothèses* (Paris: 1806), pp. 342.

G. L. Leclerc [comte de Buffon], *Oeuvres philosophiques de Buffon,* ed. J. Piveteau (Paris: Presses Universitaires de France, 1954), pp. 616.

A. P. de Candolle, *Théorie élémentaire de la botanique, ou exposition des principes de la classification naturelle et de l'art de décrire et d'étudier les végétaux* (Paris: Déterville, 1813), pp. 340.

E. Geoffroy Saint-Hilaire, *Philosophie anatomique. Des organes respiratoires* (Paris: Méquinon-Marvis, 1818), pp. 517.

—— *Principes de philosophie zoologique* (Paris: Pichon et Didier, 1830), pp. 226.

A. L. de Jussieu, *Genera plantarum* (Paris: Hérissant, 1789), pp. 498.

—— "Principes de la méthode naturelle des végétaux," *Dictionnaire des sciences naturelles* (Strasbourg-Paris: Levrault, 1824), XXX, 426–468.

J. B. de Lamarck, *Philosophie zoologique* (Paris, edition 2: Baillière, 1830), 2 vols.

—— *Discours d'ouverture (An VIII, An X, An XI, et 1806)* (Paris, 1907), pp. 157; a reprint of these lectures composing the entire volume 40 of the *Bulletin scientifique de la France et de la Belgique.*

R. Owen, *Lectures on the comparative anatomy and physiology of the invertebrate animals* (London: Longman, 1843), pp. 392.

F. Vicq-d'Azyr, *Oeuvres recueillies et publiées avec des notes et un discours sur sa vie et ses ouvrages par M. Jacques L. Moreau de la Sarthe* (Paris: Baudouin, 1805), 6 vols.

J. J. Virey, "Animal," *Nouveau dictionnaire d'histoire naturelle* (Paris: Déterville, 1803), I, 419–466.

References

Chapter I. BACKGROUNDS

1. J. J. Rousseau, quoted in G. May, *Rousseau par lui-même* (Paris, 1961), 177.

2. For details of Cuvier's early life see J. Viénot, *Georges Cuvier, Napoléon de l'intelligence* (Paris, 1932): the question of his name is discussed there, p. 1; see also the *dossier Cuvier*, Académie des sciences, Paris. The studies in Montbéliard are described by G. L. Duvernoy, *Notice historique sur les ouvrages et la vie de M. le B$^{on.}$ Cuvier* (Paris, 1833), 110 and by Cuvier in his "autobiography:" IFANF 2598(3), ff. 2–5.

3. A. F. Batz, *Description de l'Académie-Caroline de Stouttgard, librement traduite de l'original allemand composé par M. Auguste Frédéric Batz, Professeur en droit dans cette Académie* (Stuttgart, 1784), 104; IFANF 2598(3), f. 10.

4. Quoted in Viénot, *Georges Cuvier*, 76. See Ch. de Robillard de Beaurepaire, "Georges Cuvier, Secrétaire-Greffier de la commune de Bec-aux-Cauchois," *Précis des travaux de l'Académie de Rouen*, 68: 305–322 (1866).

5. [Cuvier], *Lettres de Georges Cuvier à C. H. Pfaff, 1788–1792, sur l'histoire naturelle, la politique, et la littérature. Traduites de l'allemand par Louis Marchant* (Paris, 1858), 227.

6. Quoted in Viénot, *Georges Cuvier*, 81.

7. See J. Poirier, "Georges Cuvier, second fondateur de l'Université," *Revue de Paris*, 39: 85–115 (1932); H. Puget, "Cuvier au Conseil d'état," *Revue politique et parlementaire*, 152: 300–319 (1932); L. P. Williams, "Science, education, and the French Revolution," *Isis*, 44: 311–330 (1953) and "Science, education, and Napoleon I," *Isis*, 47: 369–382 (1956).

8. IFANF 2598(3), f. 72.

9. A collected edition of these reports, plus the *Rapport historique sur les progrès des sciences naturelles depuis 1789 et sur leur état actuel* (Paris, 1810), was issued in supplementary volumes to the Baudouin edition of the complete works of Buffon (1827–1836).

10. *Life, letters, and journals of Sir Charles Lyell, Bart.*, ed. Mrs. Lyell (London, 1888), I, 249–250.

11. But see Viénot, *Georges Cuvier, passim.*

12. Cuvier, *Recueil des éloges historiques lus dans les séances publiques de l'Institut de France* (Paris, 1861), I, 119, 140, 149.

13. IFFC 295(1–5), f. 2.

14. Cuvier, "Discours de M. le Baron Cuvier [sur le prix de vertu],"

Académie Française: Recueil des discours, rapports, et pièces diverses (*1820–1829*) (Paris, 1843), 667–677; *Recueil des éloges historiques*, I, 117–149.

15. R. K. Merton, "Puritanism, pietism, and science," *Social theory and social structure* (Glencoe, Ill.: Free Press, 1949), 346.

16. Cuvier, *Discours sur les révolutions de la surface du globe et sur les changemens qu'elles ont produits dans le règne animal* (Paris, ed. 3, 1830), 4.

17. These figures are cited in tabular form by A. Cailleux, "Progression du nombre d'espèces des plantes décrites de 1500 à nos jours," *Revue d'histoire des sciences*, 6: 42–49 (1953).

18. See A. Koyré, "The significance of the Newtonian synthesis," *Archives intern. d'histoire des sciences*, no. 11, 291–311 (1950); I. B. Cohen, *Franklin and Newton* (Philadelphia: American Philosophical Society, 1956).

19. C. Linnaeus, *The elements of botany*, trans. H. Rose (London, 1775), 231.

20. *Ibid.*, 51–52.

21. *Ibid.*, 99; the order of presentation is here reversed. See N. von Hofsten, "Linnaeus's conception of nature," *Kungl. Vetenskaps-Societetens Årbok 1957* (Uppsala, 1958), 65–105; A. J. Cain, "Logic and memory in Linnaeus's system of taxonomy," *Proc. Linn. Soc. London*, *169*: 144–163 (1958).

22. G. L. Leclerc [comte de Buffon], *Oeuvres philosophiques*, ed. J. Piveteau (Paris: Presses Universitaires de France, 1954), 19, 37.

23. *Ibid.*, 236.

24. *Ibid.*, 10, 437; N. von Hofsten (reference 21), 88–89. Cf. A. O. Lovejoy, *The great chain of being* (Cambridge, Mass.: Harvard University Press, 1953), chapters VIII–IX.

25. IFANF 2598(3), ff. 3–4, 8–9.

26. Cuvier, "Prospectus," *Dictionnaire des sciences naturelles* (Strasbourg-Paris, 1816), I, vi–vii.

Chapter II. NATURE AND THE CONDITIONS OF EXISTENCE

1. Cuvier, MHN 609, § 5.

2. Cuvier, "Nature," *Dictionnaire des sciences naturelles* (Strasbourg-Paris, 1825), XXXIV, 261–268.

3. *Ibid.*, 262.

4. *Ibid.*, 267.

5. Cuvier, *Le règne animal distribué d'après son organisation* (Paris, 1817), I, 5. Also Cuvier, *Rapport historique sur les progrès des sciences depuis 1789 et sur leur état actuel* (Paris, 1810), 140.

6. MHN 609, §§ 5, 9.

7. *Rapport historique sur les progrès des sciences*, 187.

8. G. Canguilhem, "La physiologie animale," *Histoire générale des sciences*, ed. R. Taton (Paris: Presses Universitaires de France, 1958), II, 593–619.

9. [Cuvier], *Lettres de Georges Cuvier à C. H. Pfaff, 1788–1792, sur l'histoire naturelle, la politique, et la littérature. Traduites de l'allemand par Louis*

Marchant (Paris, 1858), 134; *Rapport historique sur les progrès des sciences*, 120.

10. *Rapport historique sur les progrès des sciences*, 61; E. Mendelsohn, "The controversy over the site of heat production in the body," *Proc. Amer. Philos. Soc.*, *105*: 412–420 (1961).

11. Cuvier, *Leçons d'anatomie comparée* (Paris, 1800), I, 1.

12. Cuvier, *Recueil des éloges historiques lus dans les séances publiques de l'Institut de France* (Paris, 1861), III, 44; IFFC 104, *1ᵉ leçon* [1807]; IFFC 93, f. 45.

13. *Leçons d'anatomie comparée*, I, 6–7.

14. E. S. Russell, *Form and function* (London, 1916), preface.

15. *Lettres de Georges Cuvier à C. H. Pfaff*, 71.

16. See L. J. Henderson, *The order of nature* (Cambridge, Mass., 1917); J. H. Randall, "Functional theory in biology," *Aristotle* (New York, 1960), 219–242; E. Nagel, "Teleological explanation and teleological systems," *Readings in the philosophy of science*, ed. H. Feigl and M. Brodbeck (New York: Appleton-Century-Crofts, 1953), 536–558; I. Scheffler, "Thoughts on teleology," *Brit. journ. philos. sci.*, *9*: 265–284 (1959).

17. G. G. Simpson, "The problem of plan and purpose in nature," *Sci. Monthly*, *64*: 481 (1947).

18. J. D. Logan, "The Aristotelian teleology," *Philos. review*, *6*: 386–400 (1897).

19. Cf. I. Kant, *Critique of judgement*, trans., ed., and intro. by J. H. Bernard (London, 1931).

20. *Règne animal*, I, 6.

21. For an almost complete text of the Debate of 1830 see E. Geoffroy Saint-Hilaire, *Principes de philosophie zoologique* (Paris, 1830); see also J. Piveteau, "Les discussions entre Cuvier et Geoffroy Saint-Hilaire sur l'unité de composition du règne animal," *Revue d'histoire des sciences*, *3*: 343–363 (1950).

Chapter III. COMPARATIVE ANATOMY

1. Letter, A. G. Camper to Cuvier (19 July 1800): IFFC 222(7).

2. L. J. M. Daubenton, "De la description des animaux," G. L. Leclerc [comte de Buffon], *Histoire naturelle générale et particulière* (Paris, 1753), IV, 137–138.

3. See Cuvier, "Vicq-d'Azyr, F.," *Biographie universelle* (Michaud; Paris, new ed., n. d.), XLIII, 302–305; J. F. Cabanis, "Eloge de Vicq-d'Azyr," *Oeuvres complètes de J. F. Cabanis* (Paris, 1825), V, 177–216.

4. F. Vicq-d'Azyr, *Oeuvres complètes*, ed. J. Moreau (Paris, 1805), IV, 140–141, 18–21.

5. *Ibid.*, 43–124, 233–237, 273–274.

6. Cuvier, MHN 609, *prem. partie*, separate piece.

7. Cuvier assumed full responsibility for the contents of the five volumes:

Leçons d'anatomie comparée (Paris, 1800–1805), I, xiii; III, xi. The "Discours préliminaire" which introduced the public lectures was published separately: [Cuvier], "Discours prononcé par le citoyen Cuvier, à l'ouverture de cours d'anatomie comparée qu'il fait au Muséum d'histoire naturelle pour le citoyen Mertrud," *Magasin encyclopédique*, 5: 145–155 (1795).

8. *Leçons d'anatomie comparée*, I, xv; letter, Cuvier to [?] Hartmann (18 November 1790), *Revue entomologique*, 1: 145 (1833).

9. *Leçons d'anatomie comparée*, III, xxi.

10. *Ibid.*, II, 164–165.

11. Cuvier, "Animal," *Dictionnaire des sciences médicales* (Paris, 1812), II, 142–148.

12. See F. J. Cole, *A history of comparative anatomy* (London, 1944).

13. Daubenton, reference 2, p. 130.

14. See reference 3; F. Vicq-d'Azyr, "Eloge de Camper," *Oeuvres complètes*, I, 305–322; P. M. Flourens, *Eloge historique de Jean Frédéric Blumenbach* (Paris, 1847). Also F. Vicq-d'Azyr, "Suite de recherches sur la structure du cerveau . . . Quatrième partie. Sur la structure du cerveau des animaux comparée avec celui de l'homme," *Mémoires de l'Académie des sciences*, année 1781, 468–504.

15. Cuvier, *Le règne animal distribué d'après son organisation* (Paris, 1817), I, 7; also *Leçons d'anatomie comparée*, I, v. See W. Coleman, "Les organisms marins et l'anatomie comparée *dite* expérimentale: L'oeuvre de Georges Cuvier," *Vie et milieu*, Supplementary volume (in press).

16. H. Daudin, *Les classes zoologiques et l'idée de serie animale* (Paris, 1926), II, 28 n.

17. *Leçons d'anatomie comparée*, I, 47.

18. *Ibid.*, 46

19. *Ibid.*, 49–52.

20. Cuvier and A. Valenciennes, *Histoire naturelle des poissons* (Paris, 1828), I, 201.

21. *Leçons d'anatomie comparée*, I, 51.

22. E. Geoffroy Saint-Hilaire, *Philosophie anatomique* (Paris, 1818), I, Discours préliminaire. See T. Cahn, *La vie et l'oeuvre d'Etienne Geoffroy Saint-Hilaire* (Paris, 1962); E. S. Russell, *Form and function* (London, 1916), 52–78.

23. R. Anthony, "Cuvier et la Chaire d'anatomie comparée du Muséum national d'histoire naturelle," *Arch. du Muséum*, s. 6, 9: 22 (1932).

Chapter IV. A NEW CLASSIFICATION OF ANIMALS

1. Cuvier, "Animal," *Dictionnaire des sciences naturelles* (Strasbourg-Paris, 1816), II, lii.

2. Cuvier, IFANF 2598(3), ff. 76–77.

3. Cuvier, *Le règne animal distribué d'après son organisation* (Paris, 1817), I, xvi.

REFERENCES

4. *Ibid.*, 10.

5. A. L. de Jussieu, *Genera plantarum* (Paris, 1789); a summary of these principles appeared in A. L. de Jussieu, "Principes de la méthode des végétaux," *Dictionnaire des sciences naturelles* (Strasbourg-Paris, 1824), XXX, 426–468.

6. [Cuvier], *Lettres de Georges Cuvier à C. H. Pfaff, 1788–1792, sur l'histoire naturelle, la politique, et la littérature. Traduites de l'allemand par Louis Marchant* (Paris, 1858), 247; Cuvier, *Rapport historique sur les progrès des sciences depuis 1789 et sur leur état actuel* (Paris, 1810), 287; A. L. de Jussieu, "Principes de la méthode des végétaux," 464, 431.

7. A. L. de Jussieu, "Principes de la méthode des végétaux," 447.

8. Cuvier, "Sur un nouveau rapprochement à établir entre les classes qui composent le règne animal," *Ann. du Muséum, 19*: 73 (1812).

9. *Rapport historique sur les progrès des sciences*, 291.

10. E. Geoffroy Saint-Hilaire and Cuvier, "Mémoire sur une nouvelle division des Mammifères et sur les principes qui doivent servir de base dans cette sorte de travail," *Magasin encyclopédique, 2*: 169 (1795).

11. For a detailed review of Cuvier's different classifications of the animal kingdom see H. Daudin, *Les classes zoologiques et l'idée de série animale* (Paris, 1926), I, 105–458; II, 3–68.

12. Cuvier, "Mémoire sur la structure interne et externe, et sur les affinités des animaux auxquels on a donné le nom de Vers," *Décade philosophique, 5*: 385 (1795).

13. *Ibid.*, 396.

14. Cuvier, *Tableau élémentaire de l'histoire naturelle des animaux* (Paris, 1798), 83–86.

15. *Leçons d'anatomie comparée*, I, *Premier tableau*.

16. J. J. Virey, "Animal," *Nouveau dictionnaire des sciences naturelles* (Paris, 1803), I, 419–466.

17. Cuvier, "Sur les vers qui ont le sang rouge," *Bull. scientifique de la Société philomatique*, no. 64, 121–122 (*an* 10).

18. Cuvier, IFFC 104, *cours* 1807, *Leçon* 39; *cours* 1809, *Leçon* 1.

19. "Sur un nouveau rapprochement à établir entre les classes," 76.

20. *Ibid.*

21. *Lettres de Georges Cuvier à C. H. Pfaff*, 198–199; *Règne animal*, I, 11–12.

22. IFFC 98. See Appendix A, p. 187.

23. See E. Mayr, "Species concepts and definitions," *The species problem*, ed. E. Mayr (Washington, D. C.: American Association for the Advancement of Science, 1957), 1–22.

24. Cuvier, "Prospectus" [to *Histoire naturelle des poissons* (reference 25)] (Paris, 1827), 23.

25. Cuvier and A. Valenciennes, *Histoire naturelle des poissons* (Paris, 1828), II, 17.

26. See, for example, the tables for Percoides, *ibid.*, 17–18.

27. C. Laurillard, "Georges Cuvier," *Biographie universelle* (Michaud; Paris, new ed., n. d.), IX, 594; "Prospectus" (reference 24), 20.

28. *Règne animal* (Paris, ed. 2, 1829), I, xxxiii.

29. See *Histoire naturelle des poissons*, I, 371. On the "reality" or "non-reality" of the higher categories see Cuvier, *Recueil des éloges historiques lus dans les séances publiques de l'Institut de France* (Paris, 1861), II, 119.

30. T. H. Huxley, "Owen's position in the history of anatomical science," *The life of Richard Owen*, ed. R. Owen (London, 1894), II, 284.

31. H. Daudin, *Les classes zoologiques*, II, 12–68.

32. *Ibid.*, 267–268. See also *avant-propos*, i–x.

Chapter V. THE STUDY OF FOSSIL ORGANIC REMAINS

1. Letter, A. G. Camper to Cuvier (? November 1799): IFFC 221(1); letter, Cuvier to J. H. F. Autenrieth (1 *fructidor an* 8 [1800]): Württembergische Landesbibliothek (Stuttgart), Cod. hist. gt. 413.

2. See A. Birembaut, "La minéralogie et la géologie," *Histoire de la science*, ed. M. Daumas (Paris: Gallimard, 1957), 1057–1127 (bibliography, pp. 1125–1127); M. Boule, "Georges Cuvier, fondateur de la paléontologie," *Arch. du Muséum*, s. 6, 9: 33–46 (1932).

3. Cuvier and A. Brongniart, *Essai sur la géographie minéralogique des environs de Paris avec une carte géognostique et des coupes de terrain* (Paris, 1811): Cuvier wrote ca. one-sixth of the text and Brongniart the remainder (MHN 631). See L. De Launay, *Les Brongniarts* (Paris: G. Rapilly, 1940), 87–88; A. Lacroix, "Georges Cuvier et la minéralogie," *Arch. du Muséum*, s. 6, 9: 69–76 (1932).

4. Letter, J. A. H. Reimarus to Cuvier (7 April 1797): IFFC 222(3); Cuvier, "Rapport de l'Institut national . . . sur un ouvrage de M. André, ayant pour titre: Théorie de la surface actuelle de la terre," *Journ. des mines*, 21: 413–430 (1807) [read August 1806]; IFFC 103 [*cours* of 1808]; MHN 631.

5. Cuvier, *Discours sur les révolutions de la surface du globe et sur les changemens qu'elles ont produits dans le règne animal* (Paris, ed. 3, 1830), 8, 58. See M. Boule, "La paléontologie zoologique," *La science française* [no editor] (Paris, 1915), 289–317; F. Haber, "Fossils and the idea of a process of time in natural history," *Forerunners of Darwin: 1745–1859*, ed. B. Glass, O. Temkin, and W. L. Straus (Baltimore: Johns Hopkins Press, 1959), 222–261.

6. *Discours sur les révolutions de la surface du globe*, 54–55. The order of questions is changed in the citation.

7. *Ibid.*, 60–64, 93.

8. G. L. Leclerc [comte de Buffon], *Oeuvres philosophiques*, ed. J. Piveteau (Paris: Presses Universitaires de France, 1954), 126, 202 n. 10, 123 (editor's note 10), 170.

9. Cuvier, "Mémoire sur les espèces d'éléphans vivantes et fossiles," *Mém. de l'Institut (Classe math. phys.)*, 2: 1–22 (1799).

10. *Discours sur les révolutions de la surface du globe*, 95.

11. *Ibid.*, 98–99.

12. *Ibid.*, 102, 105.

13. Cuvier, *Recherches sur les ossemens fossiles des quadrupèdes* (Paris, 1812), III: Introduction, 3 [this edition lacks continuous pagination].

14. *Ibid.*, *1ᵉ mémoire*, 1–28.

15. *Ibid.*, *3ᵉ mémoire*, 76–79.

16. *Ibid.*, 80, 82.

17. *Ibid.*, "Mémoire sur le squelette presque entier d'un petit quadrupède du genre Sarigues, trouvé dans la pierre à plâtre des environs de Paris," 1–16. This was, in fact, an inspired guess by Cuvier since not all marsupials possess these bones.

18. Among the more interesting of these memoirs are "Sur le grand animal fossile des carrières de Maestricht," *ibid.*, IV, 1–32, in which this enormous creature was proved to be structurally similar to the monitor and not to be a monstrous crocodile, and "Sur quelques quadrupèdes ovipares fossiles conservés dans les schistes calcaires: Article II. Sur le prétendu homme fossile des carrières d'OEningen, décrit par Scheuzer," *ibid.*, IV, 1–20, in which Cuvier shows that this notorious animal was a gigantic salamander (*Proteus*) and not a fossil man.

19. *Discours sur les révolutions de la surface du globe*, 108–109, 111. For the relations between fossil animals and the geological strata see pp. 108–117, 288–354.

20. *Ibid.*, 112

21. *Ibid.*, 292. See W. Smith, *A geological map of England and Wales* (London, 1815); *Stratigraphical system of organised fossils* (London, 1817); A. Brongniart, "Sur les caractères zoologiques des formations, avec l'application de ces caractères à la détermination de quelques terrains de craie," *Ann. des mines*, 6: 537–572 (1821).

22. *Discours sur les révolutions de la surface du globe*, 16–18.

23. *Ibid.*, 34, 41. Cf. *Life, letters, and journals of Sir Charles Lyell, Bart.*, ed. Mrs. Lyell (London, 1888), I, 249–250.

24. *Discours sur les révolutions de la surface du globe*, 23, 47–52.

25. *Ibid.*, 353.

26. J. A. Deluc, *Lettres philosophiques sur l'histoire de la terre et de l'homme adressées à la reine de la Grande Bretagne* (Paris-La Haye, 1779), V, part 2.

27. "Rapport sur un ouvrage de M. André" (reference 4), 422–424.

28. Sketch of a response by Cuvier (n. d.) to a letter from H. de la Fite (17 April 1824): MHN 627.

29. *Discours sur les révolutions de la surface du globe*, 27–28.

30. Cf. R. Potonié, "Zu Cuviers Kataklysmentheorie," *Paläontol. Zeitschrift*, 31: 9–14 (1957).

31. *Discours sur les révolutions de la surface du globe*, 129–130.

32. *Ibid.*, 26.

33. Buffon, *Oeuvres philosophiques* (reference 8), 138.

34. *Discours sur les révolutions de la surface du globe*, 139–165.

35. *Ibid.*, 177 n.

Chapter VI. THE SPECIES QUESTION

1. Cuvier's sudden death in 1832 deprived the historian of a major treatise apparently devoted to the refutation of the transmutation idea. Only a few pages of the Introduction to this work, "Sur la variété de composition des animaux," were completed (IFFC 65).

2. Cuvier, *Leçons d'anatomie comparée* (Paris, 1800), I, 58; Cuvier, *Le règne animal distribué d'après son organisation* (Paris, 1817), I, 18–19. For an opposing view see J. B. de Lamarck, *La philosophie zoologique* (Paris, ed. 2, 1830), I, 74.

3. Cuvier, *Discours sur les révolutions de la surface du globe et sur les changemens qu'elles ont produits dans le règne animal* (Paris, ed. 3, 1830), 119; also, *Règne animal*, I, 19.

4. [Cuvier], *Lettres de Georges Cuvier à C. H. Pfaff, 1788–1792, sur l'histoire naturelle, la politique, et la littérature. Traduites de l'allemand par Louis Marchant* (Paris, 1858), 200–201.

5. *Ibid.*, 178–179.

6. *Discours sur les révolutions de la surface du globe*, 120–121; Cuvier, *Recueil des éloges historiques lus dans les séances publiques de l'Institut de France* (Paris, 1861), I, 195; IFFC 110, f. 33.

7. *Discours sur les révolutions de la surface du globe*, 128, 125. See "Rapport des professeurs du Muséum sur les collections d'histoire naturelle rapportées d'Egypte par E. Geoffroy [Saint-Hilaire]," *Ann. du Muséum*, *1*: 236 (1802).

8. Cuvier, "Mémoire sur les Cloportes terrestres," *Journ. d'histoire naturelle*, *2*: 18 (1792).

9. Cuvier and A. Valenciennes, *Histoire naturelle des poissons* (Paris, 1828), I, 568–569.

10. *Règne animal*, I, xx; *Leçons d'anatomie comparée*, I, 58–60; Cuvier, "Sur un nouveau rapprochement à établir entre les classes qui composent le règne animal," *Ann. du Muséum*, *19*: 79, 81 (1812).

11. *Histoire naturelle des poissons*, I, 570.

12. *Discours sur les révolutions de la surface du globe*, 120.

13. Cf. L. Eiseley, *Darwin's century. Evolution and the men who discovered it* (Garden City, N. Y.: Doubleday, 1958), 88–115, 353; R. Hooykaas, *Natural law and divine miracle* (Leiden: E. J. Brill, 1958), 98, 200–202.

14. E. Bréhier, *Histoire de la philosophie allemande* (Paris, 1921), 92.

15. See Chapter II, reference 21. Also W. Lubosch, "Die Akademiestreit zwischen Geoffroy Saint-Hilaire und Cuvier im Jahre 1830 und seine leitenden Gedanken," *Biol. Centralblatt*, *38*: 357–384, 397–456 (1918).

REFERENCES

16. Cuvier, "Sur la composition de la tête osseuse dans les animaux vertébrés," *Arch. du Muséum, 19*: 123–128 (1812).

17. Cuvier, "Le crâne est-il un vertèbre?," MHN 606, *deux. partie.*

18. *Leçons d'anatomie comparée* (Paris, ed. 2, 1835), I, 60–63.

19. Cuvier, "Nature," *Dictionnaire des sciences naturelles* (Strasbourg-Paris, 1825), XXXIV, 265.

20. R. Owen, *Lectures on the comparative anatomy and physiology of the invertebrate animals* (London, 1843), 379. See G. G. Simpson, "Anatomy and morphology: classification and evolution: 1859 and 1959," *Proc. Amer. Philos. Soc., 103*: 286–306 (1959).

21. C. Darwin, *On the origin of species by means of natural selection* (London, ed. 2, 1860), 413–414.

22. *Histoire naturelle des poissons*, I, 550.

23. IFFC 65, f. 114. Also IFFC 104, *1e leçon*; Cuvier, "Considérations sur les Mollusques, et en particulier sur les Céphalopodes," *Ann. des sciences naturelles, 19*: 247 (1830).

24. Cuvier and C. Duméril, "Rapport sur un mémoire de M. Roulin, ayant pour objet la découverte d'une nouvelle espèce de tapir dans l'Amérique du sud, fait à l'Académie royale des sciences [13 April 1829]," *Ann. des sciences naturelles, 17*: 109–110 (1829).

25. Lamarck, *Philosophie zoologique* (reference 2), I, 75–81. See P. Ostoya, *Les théories de l'évolution* (Paris, 1951), 64–93; Cuvier's disparaging but still valuable *éloge* of Lamarck, *Recueil des éloges historiques*, III, 179–210.

26. Lamarck, *Philosophie zoologique*, I, 222.

27. *Recueil des éloges historiques*, III, 200.

28. *Leçons d'anatomie comparée* (Paris, ed. 2, 1835), I, 100–101.

29. Lamarck, *Philosophie zoologique*, I, 369; *Recueil des éloges historiques*, III, 201.

30. *Histoire naturelle des poissons*, I, 543.

31. W. Coleman, "Lyell and the 'reality' of the species, 1830–1833," *Isis, 53*: 325–338 (1962).

32. H. Metzger, *La genèse de la science des cristaux* (Paris, 1918), 93–124.

33. See E. Genet-Varcin, "La génération des êtres vivants d'après Buffon," *Buffon*, ed. R. Heim (Paris: Editions du Muséum, 1952), 149–150.

34. Reading notes (to what work?) in Cuvier's hand, Wellcome Medical Historical Library (London): MS. 67391.

35. Cuvier, *Rapport historique sur les progrès des sciences depuis 1789 et sur leur état actuel* (Paris, 1810), 193, 194.

36. See E. S. Russell, *Form and function* (London, 1916), *passim.*

37. "Nature" (reference 19), 266–267.

38. *Règne animal* (Paris, ed. 2, 1829), I, 69.

39. Cf. IFFC 102, 2e, 3e *leçons.*

40. *Règne animal* (Paris, ed. 2, 1829), I, 80.

41. *Ibid.*, 64; IFFC 102, 6e, 7e *leçons.*

REFERENCES

42. *Recueil des éloges historiques*, II, 184–186.
43. *Discours sur les révolutions de la surface du globe*, 171–172.
44. See E. Carteilhac, "Georges Cuvier et l'ancienneté de l'homme," *Matériaux pour l'histoire naturelle et primitive de l'homme* (Paris, 1884), 27–45; P. Lester, "La paléontologie humaine," *Histoire de la science*, ed. M. Daumas (Paris: Gallimard, 1957), 1407–1432.
45. *Discours sur les révolutions de la surface du globe*, 68.
46. P. Lester, "L'anthropologie," *Histoire de la science*, ed. M. Daumas (Paris: Gallimard, 1957), 1367. See W. Stanton, *The leopard's spots. Scientific attitudes towards race in America, 1815–1859* (Chicago: University of Chicago Press, 1960), *passim*.

Chapter VII. CUVIER AND EVOLUTION

1. J. Bronowski, *The common sense of science* (Cambridge, Mass.: Harvard University Press, 1953), 48.
2. Cuvier, *Leçons d'anatomie comparée* (Paris, ed. 2, 1835), I, 64.
3. Cuvier, IFFC 94, ff. 382–383. See Appendix B, p. 189.
4. E. Mayr, "Species concepts and definitions," *The species problem*, ed. E. Mayr (Washington, D. C.: American Association for the Advancement of Science, 1957), 2.
5. Cf. S. Toulmin, *Foresight and understanding* (Bloomington: Indiana University Press, 1961), 91–92.
6. R. Hooykaas, *Natural law and divine miracle* (Leiden: E. J. Brill, 1959), 198.
7. J. Dillenberger, *Protestant thought and natural science* (Garden City, N. Y.: Doubleday, 1960), 136–137. See C. C. Gillispie, *Genesis and geology* (Cambridge, Mass.: Harvard University Press, 1951); C. E. Raven, *Science and religion* (Cambridge: Cambridge University Press, 1953).
8. Cuvier, *Discours sur les révolutions de la surface du globe et sur les changemens qu'elles ont produits dans le règne animal* (Paris, ed. 3, 1830), 82–83. Cf. A. Houtin, *La question biblique chez les catholiques de France au XIXᵉ siècle* (Paris, 1902), 136–137.
9. IFFC 91, ff. 150–151; IFFC 92, ff. 7–9.
10. Cuvier, *Recueil des éloges historiques lus dans les séances publiques de l'Institut de France* (Paris, 1861), III, 272.
11. A. D. d'Orbigny, *Cours élémentaire de paléontologie et de géologie stratigraphique* (Paris, 1849), I, *passim;* T. H. Huxley, "Paleontology and the doctrine of evolution," *Discourses biological and geological* (New York, 1897), 354–355.

Index